TAPPING THE BOW

ISBN 0-88925-590-3

Published by
Eastern Irrigation District
P.O. Box 8
Brooks, Alberta T0J 0J0
Canada

Publication of this book was assisted by a publishing grant from Alberta Culture.

First printing, 1985

Unless otherwise credited, all illustrations are the property of the Eastern Irrigation District Archives and Library.

Printed and bound in Canada by
Friesen Printers
a Division of D. W. Friesen & Sons Ltd.
Ste. 120, 3016-19th Street N.E.
Calgary, Alberta T2E 6Y9
Canada

Head Office
Altona, Manitoba R0G 0B0
Canada

AUTHORS' ACKNOWLEDGEMENTS

The production of this book was immeasurably aided by the generous assistance of many people.

Personnel of the following institutions gave freely of their time and knowledge to direct us to research materials and/or photographs held in their collections: the Glenbow Museum; Provincial Archives of Alberta; Alberta Legislature Library; City of Lethbridge, Sir Alexander Galt Museum and Archives; Lethbridge Northern Irrigation District; the public relations department of Canadian Pacific Limited, Calgary; Brooks Municipal Public Library; Brooks and District Museum; Brooks Bulletin; Alberta Agriculture; Prairie Farm Rehabilitation Administration; Alberta Horticultural Research Centre; Brooks Wildlife Centre; Southeast Alberta Regional Planning Commission; Ducks Unlimited Canada; Alberta Wheat Pool; Dinosaur Provincial Park; Underwood McLellan Ltd; Public Works Historical Society, Chicago; and the Bureau of Reclamation, Washington, D.C.

The Eastern Irrigation District Archives and Library was a rich source of information and photographs. This recently-established facility promises to be one of which the residents of the EID may be proud, as it will be an important resource for all future students of Alberta's agricultural development.

It would take several pages to list local residents who were unstinting in their efforts to help us. They shared their recollections of how our history was shaped, and gave us access to their personal papers, documents and photographs. Many of them reviewed the manuscript, either in whole or in part.

Working with the staff of the Eastern Irrigation District has been a pleasure. They have given us the benefit of their knowledge in all aspects of the organization's operations and responded cheerfully to our many requests for advice and assistance. To them, and to all who have helped in any way with the research and writing of *Tapping the Bow*, we express our thanks.

We appreciate the support and encouragement shown us by the Eastern Irrigation District Board of Directors.

Finally, to our husbands, our gratitude for their forbearance during this bout of workaholism.

FROM THE EID BOARD OF DIRECTORS TO THE PEOPLE OF THE EASTERN IRRIGATION DISTRICT:

L. to R.: R. Peltzer, J. Walde, J. Chomistek, Jr., Chairman D. Alberts, D. Giles, J. Veenstra, W. Mortensen.

As your Board of Directors in this milestone year, we are pleased to present to you this history in celebration of the 50th anniversary of the Eastern Irrigation District.

The book is intended as a permanent record to honour the combined efforts of all those who have participated in our district's success, throughout the years since our organization was formed. Among these we include: the CPR builders of our irrigation system; the pioneers who worked to transfer ownership of the system from the CPR to the district farmers; the water users who served before us as trustees and directors; all EID employees, both current and past; the farming families, whose personal success has contributed to the prosperity of the district as a whole; all the people who have made their homes within the borders of the Eastern Irrigation District; and, finally, the farmers and ranchers from the surrounding areas who add a dryland dimension to the agricultural resources of our community.

FOREWORD

This is an intriguing and well-researched story of the development by determined people of a considerable portion of the arid land known as the Palliser Triangle.

The pioneering efforts of the early settlers on CPR land trying to build homes, roads, schools and decent communities are well described. The frustration of attempting to live up to CPR land contracts in the depression years of 1922-27 and 1930-35, might make one wonder — could this be true? As one who experienced the day-to-day existence of those years, I can testify that the authors have not exaggerated our troubles.

The story tells, in compelling fashion, of how we farmers, determined to improve our situation, banded together and took over the irrigation system.

Under revised land contracts, negotiated between the new Eastern Irrigation District and the farmers, the settlers forged ahead. Our district's success is a positive example of the benefits to be derived when a group of people work together for the good of all.

In their history of the irrigation project, the authors lead the reader to understand an important principle — that irrigation farmers, with their high cost of production, should not be burdened with the capital cost of the project. The CPR's resistance to this idea contributed to the growing pains of the district. Since 1935 when the EID was formed, recognition has been given to this principle and has become the basis of irrigation policy for both the federal and provincial governments.

Truly, this is an indispensable book for students, researchers, historians, engineers, irrigation specialists and agriculturists, or for that matter, anyone interested in a good story.

Carl J. Anderson

TABLE OF CONTENTS

INTRODUCTION

The landscape of the Eastern Irrigation District in southern Alberta evokes a sense of order and permanence. Like grids on a map unbending roads mark off the fields, bestowing a predictable geometric regularity upon the flat expanse. In the growing season, under the widest of clear blue skies, acres of gold-ripening grains ripple in the persistent breezes, placid cattle fatten on rich, green pastures and the abundant foliage of tall trees casts shade over substantial farmsteads.

Such a pastoral scene speaks of generation upon generation of man in harmony with the land. Yet, still living in the District today are some who played a vital role in its creation and others, more numerous, who contributed to its development.

The earliest settlers knew the land in its untamed state. It was a rolling treeless plain, its vast spaces punctuated by low clumps of cactus, sagebrush and wild prairie rose. Only the survey stakes protruding from the earth at the four corners of each quarter-section gave a hint of the high hopes held for its future.

The transformation began about seventy years ago when the first irrigation water was delivered to the land through a complex of canals fed from the Bow River. Over the years since then, the labour of a farming population with belief in itself and in the ultimate benefits of irrigation has converted a "dry and barren land where no water is" into one of the most productive agricultural communities in Canada.

The area that now is the Eastern Irrigation District was once part of the final payment of land made by the Dominion of Canada to the Canadian Pacific Railway Company for building the first Canadian trans-continental railway. Between the years of 1910 and 1914, it was the scene of a construction boom as men flooded in to work on the structures of a system billed as "one of the greatest irrigation projects of modern times."

The water ran down the ditches in 1914 as planned and settlement began in a spirit of confidence. But a world war was followed by an agricultural recession that began in the 1920's and deepened into the debilitating depression of the "Dirty Thirties." In less than a decade, the bright promise of the project had tarnished. Many of the original settlers abandoned their farms and moved on. New families succeeded them and then they, too, gave up and went away. But amid all the dislocations was a core who clung tenaciously to their dream. They were faced with the harsh fact that they simply could not realize enough profit from their farms to meet the payments on the contracts they had made for the purchase of their land from the CPR. Debt-ridden and unable to see an end to the plight in which they found themselves, yet not prepared to give up, they banded together to search for solutions.

All was not rosy for the CPR, either. The company suffered heavy operating losses and saw little hope for any short-term recovery of its large capital investment in the project. When the idea of the farmers assuming responsibility for the water delivery system evolved from negotiations between them and the CPR, both sides greeted the prospect with some relief. With advice and guidance from the Irrigation Council of the Government of Alberta, the CPR was relieved of the onus of water delivery and maintenance of the system. The irrigation works, the existing land contracts and the unsold lands of the project, together with a fund of $300,000 were transferred into the hands of the farmers' organization. On May 1st, 1935, the Eastern Irrigation District was born.

Today, we look back with admiration at the foresight of the farmers who formed our organization. We take justifiable pride in the forward strides we have made in the 50 years since then. Together, we have built a stable community that attests to the benefits of irrigation.

In latter years, our success story has moved beyond the narrow confines of our District. There has been a growing awareness on the part of government of the contribution irrigation makes, not just to those who farm "under the ditch" but to the larger economic community.

An infusion of funds from both the federal and provincial governments has allowed the Eastern Irrigation District to make improvements to the existing system. With the assistance of enlightened governments willing to invest in the future of irrigation, the Eastern Irrigation District stands poised on the threshold of new and exciting opportunities in its history.

On a map, the water delivery system is a network of meandering lines snaking out over the area drawn to represent the EID. In its work-a-day reality, it is a canal system that brings water to a thirsty land. On another plane, it has a deeper significance. It is a symbol of dreams and aspirations — of the CPR whose vision built it, of the pioneer farmers whose faith in its worth led to the creation of the EID, and of the many men and women who have made their homes and prospered under the life-enhancing gift of its water.

A golden anniversary is a very special occasion. It is a celebration of the events that shaped our history. It is a time to assess the present and to anticipate a future in which we, in our day, have the opportunity to build on the legacy of those who went before us.

Typical land pattern in EID.

PART I
IRRIGATION AT WORK IN
THE EID

Modern rehabilitated canals are seen throughout the District. This one is a secondary canal on the Rolling Hills part of the irrigation system.

The perimeter of the Eastern Irrigation District encloses nearly 1.5 million acres (600,000 ha), an area considerably larger than the entire land mass occupied by Prince Edward Island. Its boundary in the north follows the path of the Red Deer River from 50 miles (80 km) upstream of Dinosaur Provincial Park through to the Park's eastern extremity; from here, it runs due south along the line between Ranges 10 and 11 for 45 miles (70 km). At that point, the boundary makes a ninety-degree turn to the west to connect with the Bow River, following the irregular course of this stream to 3 miles (5 km) south-west of Bassano. A jogging north-easterly line from this point back to the Red Deer River completes the enclosure of the block.

The Eastern Irrigation District is one of 13 irrigation districts in Alberta. It is unique among these by virtue of the fact that it owns a large amount of land within the area served by its water delivery system, as well as the structures of the system itself. With landownership comes a set of concerns not shared by the other irrigation districts: payment of taxes, and land development and administration. Of the total area contained within the block, 845,000 acres (345,000 ha) are owned by individual water users. The remaining land is owned collectively by the 1180 water users who make up the membership of the EID. From among their number, they elect a board of seven directors to oversee the operation and maintenance of the irrigation system and the management of the commonly-held lands. With title to approximately 640,000 acres (259,000 ha), the EID is Alberta's largest private landowner.

The Eastern Irrigation District lies on the highest of the three prairie levels, or steppes. All three levels slope gradually in an easterly direction from the heights of the Rocky Mountains on the west, down to the flat, featureless prairie near the Manitoba/Ontario border. The highest steppe is defined by the foothills on the west, while its eastern extremity is formed by the escarpment known as the Missouri Coteau. This ridge cuts through central Saskatchewan in a north-westerly direction.

Comprehensive surveys taken in preparation for the construction of the Eastern Section of the CPR irrigation project which now serves the EID showed that the topography of the land lends itself to a gravity system of irrigation. It is a gently rolling plain gradually descending in elevation from west to east. The highest elevation is in its western part, about 2,800 feet (853 m) above sea level, and it drops off to 2,400 feet (732 m) above sea level at its eastern end.

Generally, the Red Deer River is several hundred feet lower than the Bow River. From the main divide of the watershed between the two rivers, the land slopes more steeply toward the Red Deer. Several deep valleys cut straight across the country from river to river. The summit of one of these valleys, the Crawling Valley, coincides with the main divide at a point near the Bow River. It was decided that a canal cutting through the main divide here would be high enough and far enough from the Red Deer River to provide water, diverted from the Bow River, to a large area of land lying between the two.

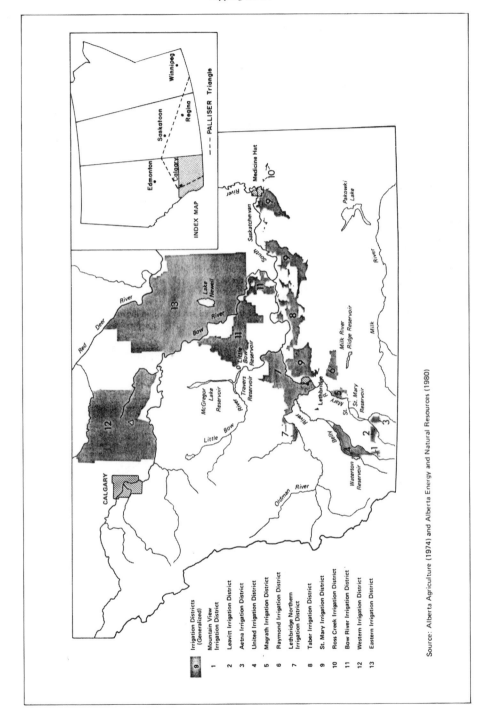

INDEX MAP

Edmonton
Saskatoon
Winnipeg
Regina
Calgary
--- PALLISER Triangle

CALGARY

Medicine Hat

South Saskatchewan River

Pakowki Lake

Milk River

Milk River Ridge Reservoir

Red Deer River

Bow River

Lake Newell

Little Bow River

Travers Reservoir

Little Bow Reservoir

McGregor Lake Reservoir

St. Mary Reservoir

St. Mary River

Belly River

Waterton Reservoir

Lethbridge

Oldman River

Irrigation Districts (Generalized)

1 Mountain View Irrigation District
2 Leavitt Irrigation District
3 Aetna Irrigation District
4 United Irrigation District
5 Magrath Irrigation District
6 Raymond Irrigation District
7 Lethbridge Northern Irrigation District
8 Taber Irrigation District
9 St. Mary Irrigation District
10 Ross Creek Irrigation District
11 Bow River Irrigation District
12 Western Irrigation District
13 Eastern Irrigation District

Source: Alberta Agriculture (1974) and Alberta Energy and Natural Resources (1980)

THE DIVERSION: BASSANO DAM

The Bow River runs in a deeply incised valley and the engineering challenge facing the designers of the project was to raise the water level sufficiently to facilitate its flow into the main canal. Bassano Dam, built to serve this function, was sited to take advantage of a long horseshoe bend on the river. The banks of the inner side of this bend, now submerged by the pool of dammed water, were very much lower than the outer banks of the river channel. A dam built in the channel would have simply caused the river to change course and flow out over the inner banks and across the low land lying in the curve of the horseshoe. To prevent this, a composite structure was designed consisting of a concrete spillway built in the original river channel, and a high, earthen embankment which extends from the south end of the spillway across the foot of the horseshoe.

The spillway portion of the structure is a hollow overflow dam made of reinforced concrete and structural steel. It is supported by a series of parallel triangular buttresses which are sloped from top to bottom at a 45-degree angle on the upstream side. The crest of the dam is curved and, on the downstream side, it extends into an apron which corresponds to the path of the water flowing over the crest. The dam spillway is built on a concrete floor laid on the clay of the streambed. The maximum height from the floor to the overflow crest is 40 feet (12 m). Rising above this are sluice gates which control the flow of water over the crest.

The earthen portion of the dam stretches from the south side of the spillway across the horseshoe. It has a width at the base of 350 feet (100 m) and, at its highest point, measures 45 feet (14 m). Building the embankment entailed the moving of over 10 million cubic feet (300,000 m³) of earth, most of which came from the excavation of the main canal through which water is channelled out to the distribution system. The headgates for this intake canal are located at the north side of the spillway. At this point, the height of the water is 46 feet (14 m) above the original river level.

Building of the irrigation structures began in 1910. Some of the work, by necessity, was seasonal. As the dam was the focal point of the system, every effort was made to keep its construction rolling throughout the year. Excavation was done by horse teams, wagons and slip scrapers. Heavy frost was a hindrance to progress, so a method was devised to counteract its effects. At night, large tarpaulins, supported by a horse at each corner, were stretched over the area intended for excavation the following day. Numerous small stoves, called sala-manders, were kept stoked through the night; and, by morning, the ground was thawed sufficiently for work to proceed. Concrete work was suspended only when the thermometer fell to 15 degrees below zero Fahrenheit ($-26°C$). In four years, the major structures of the irrigation system were completed.

Sir Thomas Shaughnessy, the President of the Canadian Pacific Railway, opened the dam on April 26, 1914. Bassano Dam was considered noteworthy in

1914 for its composite character, its great length (the spillway section is 720 feet [220 m] long, the earthen embankment extends 7,000 feet [2,200 m] beyond the spillway), and for the quantity of water which could be accommodated over its crest at flood (a flow of 100,000 cubic feet [3000 m³] per second could pass through the opened sluice gates without danger of damage to the structure).

Sweeping view of Bassano Dam on horsehoe bend of Bow River.

HUGH B. MUCKLESTON

The design for the Bassano Dam was the work of Hugh B. Muckleston, the CPR engineer most closely associated with the Eastern Section of the irrigation project. Some artists have insisted that a work of art should be judged only on its own merit, allowing no quarter for its maker's personal history. In a sense, this is what has happened in Muckleston's case, whether or not he wished it. His creations have become familiar landmarks while he, himself, has faded into obscurity. What is known of him is that he was employed by the CPR in 1898, first as a rodman and later as a leveller on the rail line through the Crowsnest Pass. In 1902, he was fired for an error in locating a pier in the Kootenay Bridge. The mistake could not have been judged too grave as he was rehired in 1903 in the capacity of engineer and assigned to the early irrigation surveys of the

Eastern Section. As assistant to Chief Engineer A. S. Dawson, Muckleston drew up the plans for all the major structures of the irrigation system, although the detailed plans for the Brooks Aqueduct were the work of G. M. Gibb. The first world war, in which he reached the rank of major, took Muckleston away from the area. He returned after the war for a short time; then, in 1920, he resigned from the CPR to take up the duties of chief engineer for the Lethbridge Northern Irrigation District. Perhaps it is not surprising that among the hundreds of engineers employed by the CPR, Muckleston does not stand out. Beyond the bare facts given here, nothing is known of his personal life. But for the people of the Eastern Irrigation District, his importance is unparalleled. Suffice it to say, that when the water runs down the ditches in the spring, thanks are due to this unsung hero.

Bassano Dam has proved to be a well-designed structure for the diversion of water. Damage and wear have, of course, occurred in the seventy-odd years since it was first put into operation. Standards of maintenance have been good but the dam is showing its age. Concrete has a life span; and, in time, climatic effects take their toll and it becomes weak. The portions of the spillway above water level are especially susceptible to alternate freezing and thawing conditions. In 1980, major repair work was undertaken on the dam by the Government of Canada through the Prairie Farm Rehabiliation Administration (PFRA). The plan, initially, was to upgrade the dam sufficiently to extend its life by 10 years, during which time a new water diversion structure would be built. Subsequently, the plan for a new structure was deferred. It was decided to concentrate more funds to recondition the dam completely and, thereby, guarantee its efficiency for the foreseeable future.

In addition to replacing weakened concrete in the spillway and rebuilding to strengthen the earthen portion of the dam, the plan calls for the replacement of the present sluice gates. A modern, automatically-regulated gate system will be used to control the flow of water over the crest of the spillway. Surges in the river flow are common and, under the present system, water flow may increase or recede with little warning. Delays or misjudgment in setting the gates can mean that water, which could have been diverted to make up shortages in the distribution system, is lost over the dam. Conversely, more water may be diverted than the irrigation system can handle economically, with the result that much of it simply passes through the system and returns via drainage channels to the Red Deer or Bow Rivers. Obviously, neither of these scenarios is desirable. With the new computerized system, the control gates will regulate automatically to accommodate the changeable flow conditions of the river. This is a tremendous forward stride in water conservation and management.

–BASSANO · DAM–

PHOTOGRAPHS

Showing progress of Construction and
subsequent matters concerning floods,
protection work, repairs, etc.

Excavating Main Canal, 1910.

Work begins on earthen portion of dam. Excavated material from Main Canal carried by train along trestles.

Progress to Oct. 1911. Note how construction is phased to allow continual river flow.

Assembling formwork prior to pouring concrete spillway sill.

Progress to June 1912. Concrete spillway nearing completion.

Two days prior to dam opening. Cableway and trestle removed. Gates in place to build up river level.

Train continues to transport earth fill to west.

Placing concrete blocks and rock-filled wire crates below apron to impede erosive rush of water.

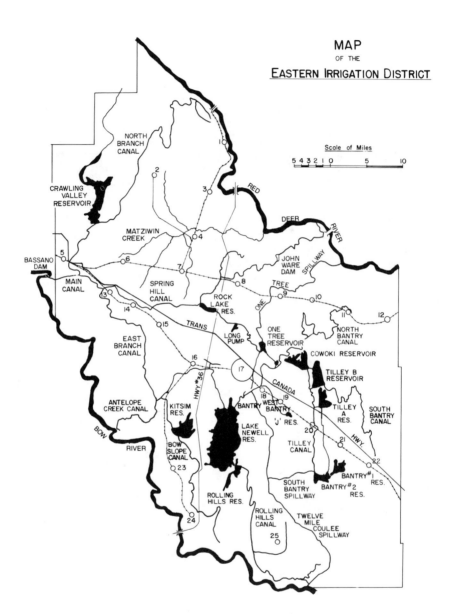

MAP
OF THE
EASTERN IRRIGATION DISTRICT

THE DISTRIBUTION SYSTEM

The District's water license allows for the diversion of 562,000 acre-feet of water from the Bow River during the irrigation season. In addition, 200,000 acre-feet are available to fill the internal reservoirs in the off-season. The storage capacity of these structures is 325,000 acre-feet. (An acre-foot is the amount of water required to cover an acre of land to the depth of one foot.)

An open-channel delivery system consisting of 342 miles (550 km) of main canals and 844 miles (1,350 km) of secondary canals brings water to 245,000 acres (99,000 ha) of land. With the opening of Crawling Valley Reservoir in 1985, the District will be able to extend irrigation to an additional 40,000 acres (16,200 ha). Some 940 miles (1,500 km) of drainage channels have been designed to carry away excess irrigation waters from the surface of the soil. Portions of these return flows are reused in some parts of the District, the remaining volumes run through a complex of drains which lead ultimately to the naturally-occurring major drainage channels of the District. In the northwest, Matziwin Creek and, in the northeast, One Tree Creek dump into the Red Deer River. Twelve Mile Coulee drains the south-east area of the District into the Bow River.

From Bassano Dam, a five-mile (eight-km) intake canal runs to Little Dam whence the main canals of the distribution system branch off. The direction of their flow is conveyed in their rather prosaic names — the North Branch Canal and

Little Dam. North Branch Canal (bottom centre) and East Branch Canal (upper left) go their separate ways.

the East Branch Canal. A short distance downstream, the East Branch Canal forks to supply water to the third main delivery channel of the system, the Spring Hill Canal. Below the Spring Hill Canal fork, water is diverted from the East Branch Canal into the Bow Slope Canal System. Before eventually emptying into Lake Newell, the East Branch also supplies water to the Cassils area and to a portion of the irrigated land around Brooks.

Within the larger framework of the irrigation network, five interdependent and interconnected canal systems operate to serve the various regions of the EID. How novel a trip via canal from one part of the District to another would be. Unfortunately, the gates and checks, which regulate water flow, bar this as a physical possibility — but travel in the imagination is free of all hindrance. What follows is just such a journey along the inland waterways of the EID.

The District is a fascinating mosaic. Each area has a distinctive personality formed of the nature of its landscape and the backgrounds of its people. Each brings its individual imprint to the stamp of the EID as a whole. In the passages below, only the briefest of community sketches are drawn; they are but a hint of richly detailed word pictures available. Thanks to the efforts of many residents, the particular events which shaped our communities have been fully recorded in local histories.

Original CPR structures.

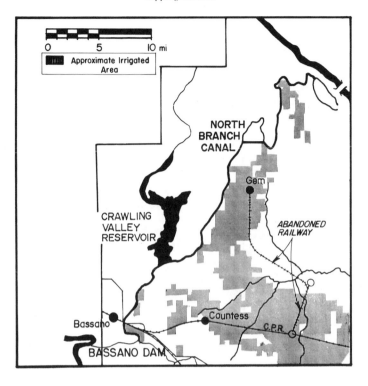

THE NORTH BRANCH CANAL SYSTEM

ITS STRUCTURES

The North Branch is the smallest of the three main canals. It follows the west flank of Crawling Valley for about 23 miles (37 km) to where it crosses the deep gorge of the valley by way of a wood-staved, trestled flume. Once the filling of Crawling Valley is completed in 1985, the flume will be phased out of operation. Its function will be taken over by a canal flowing from the reservoir. The waters of the North Branch Canal System continue on in a northerly direction, finally tailing off to the Red Deer River. Tributaries flow out to irrigate the land to the west and north of Matziwin Creek.

The idea of using the Crawling Valley as a storage site has been around since 1925. At that time, the CPR investigated it in connection with the generation of power. Since that plan called for a year-round flow of water from the Bassano Dam, it was carried no further. Water deficits along the North Branch Canal and the need for more internal storage to assist in the regulation of water supplies within the Eastern Irrigation District system revived interest in the site. In 1954, at the request of the EID, the PFRA drew up plans for the reservoir. Because of lack of funds, these documents were left to gather dust on the shelf. Government policy changed in the 1970's to reflect an increasing recognition of the importance of irrigation. One of the benefits accruing to the EID from this change was the decision to allocate funds to proceed with the building of Crawling Valley Reservoir. Construction was begun in 1983 and the first water was run into the reservoir in the fall of 1984. Design of the structure was the work of PFRA engineers. It was funded by the Alberta Heritage Savings Trust Fund, through Alberta Environment.

The reservoir has a storage capacity of 90,000 acre-feet of usable water. Its primary function is to aid in regulating the water supply throughout the entire system. It has particular significance for the area adjacent to it. At present, water

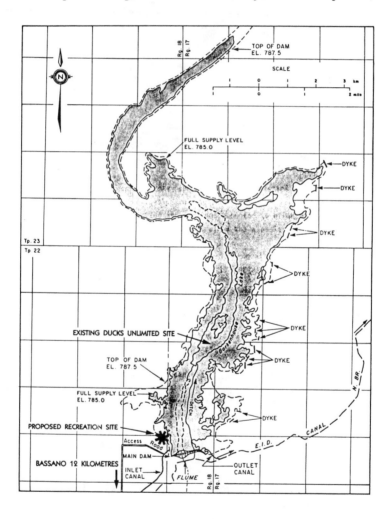

CRAWLING VALLEY DEVELOPMENT

Crawling Valley Flume on North Branch Canal System.

from the North Branch Canal irrigates the land in the Gem area. Crawling Valley Reservoir assures an adequate water supply to this area and allows for an additional 40,000 acres (16,200 ha) along the canal below the reservoir to be brought under irrigation.

Since the early planning stages Crawling Valley Reservoir was intended as a multi-use facility. A large body of water in a dry inland area inevitably draws the eager attention of those involved in providing recreational opportunities to the public. To develop the recreational potential of the reservoir, an enthusiastic group of Bassano and area residents formed the Crawling Valley Recreation Society. With the endorsement of the County of Newell, a 12-year lease agreement was made with the EID for one-quarter section of land and the society was given a capital grant, along with an annual operating grant, under the Alberta Municipal Recreation Areas Program.

The Eastern Irrigation District is very supportive of the development of this facility for recreational use. In the fall of 1984, the District undertook the earth-moving work to prepare a naturally-occurring four-acre (1.6 ha) basin for use as a swimming pool. This land-locked swimming pool is adjacent to, but separate from, the reservoir; it will be fed from a canal fitted with a gate structure. This control will be used to regulate the water level in the pool.

Alberta Environment has contributed work of like value. Through their efforts, the approach to a large boat launch and an access road have been built. Gravel for the camping grounds is to be provided by the County of Newell.

In the spring of 1985, the Recreation Society will complete work on the swimming pool, build the boat launch, and landscape the grounds. It is planned that the first phase of a four-phase plan for the construction of camping facilities will provide 30 campsites for visitors by the summer of 1985.

With the co-operation of the EID, Alberta Environment and the County of Newell, the Crawling Valley Recreation Society is well on the way to creating a much-needed water sport, picnicking and camping area which will add greatly to the attraction of the District as a whole and, in particular, to the Bassano area.

ITS COMMUNITIES

"Best in the West by a Damsite." This catchy slogan was adopted in 1911 by the first incorporated village in the EID. Bassano was at the eye of the initial storm of irrigation activity. The CPR land sales office was located here and settlement radiated out beyond the rapidly expanding townsite. By 1911, the population was over 500 and growing. In the Henderson Directory of that year, a newspaper, two banks, two hotels and a drug store were among the several businesses listed. School enrollment doubled between the 1911 and 1912 terms.

Optimism knew no bounds. The Board of Trade was dedicated to unstinting promotion of Bassano's attractions, its activities were bolstered in print on the pages of *The Bassano News*. Typical of the spirit which infused the young settlement is this newspaper quote from October 7, 1910:

> The town is going to be made in spite of itself. If you happen to be anywhere around Alberta next year and don't poke your fingers in your ears, you will hear a steady insistent humming sound. That will be Bassano growing.

As early as 1908, Bassano was an important railway and commercial centre for homesteaders flocking to take up lands north of the Red Deer and south of the Bow. Before the irrigation system was in operation, a number of dryland farms had been established on CPR lands. It was from the Bassano post office that the colourful Colonel Felix Warren, later a set designer for Hollywood Westerns, transported the mail by stagecoach to points north. The comings and goings of tourists from many parts of the globe, attracted by an important irrigation system in the making, spark the pages of the weekly newspaper in the early years.

The first group of settlers to irrigated lands in what is now the EID arrived at Bassano by rail in 1914. Their farms were located in the Gem area. The people of Bassano spared no effort to make the newcomers welcome. More about these pioneer farmers is related in the section of this book dealing with early settlement.

Although Bassano retained its position as a commercial centre for the area, the small community of Gem developed to meet the day-to-day needs of its surrounding settlers. For many years, road communication with Bassano was by way of a rough dirt trail along the flank of Crawling Valley. Building of a railway spur line to connect Gem with larger market centres was delayed until the late 1920's. It was at that time, too, that the first grain elevator was built at Gem. Prior to that, harvest time saw a steady daily caravan of grain-filled wagons making its slow progress to the shipping point at Bassano.

Today, Gem is a tiny hamlet of 34 residents. For such a small community, it has a surprising number of facilities. A hall and recreation area are gathering spots for the surrounding population. The local school provides education for Grades One through Nine. A store and post office have operated in Gem since its earliest days. Gem Mennonite and Gem Presbyterian churches serve the spiritual needs of the community.

The geographical setting of Bassano dictated its development. Although the CPR retained an office in Bassano, its headquarters was moved to the more central location of Brooks in 1918. Bassano did not reach the heights of prosperity envisioned for it by its early promoters, but it has grown steadily. With a population of 1,200, it is the only town, other than Brooks, in the District.

Situated as it is on the western edge of the District, Bassano draws its trade from the wheat farming and cattle raising area lying west and north of the town, from ranching operations to its south, as well as from the irrigated lands in its vicinity. A primary feed processing plant and a feedlot for beef calves cater to the livestock growers.

The other main agricultural industry in Bassano is a growers' co-operative where potatoes and other vegetables are packed and processed for shipment. Its main product is potatoes; between 8,000 and 10,000 tons (7 and 9 million kg) are packaged yearly, largely for the Alberta market. Farmers in the Rainier, Rosemary and Duchess areas are the main producers. Co-operatives, organized to abet marketing, were once common in the District. One after another, they ceased to exist and the potato growers' co-op is one of the few remaining organizations of this kind.

Electrical parts manufactured in a small plant in Bassano are used in thermoelectric power stations around the world.

There is a wide range of social agencies, educational services and recreational facilities in Bassano.

The name "Countess" is often mentioned in accounts of early settlement in the District. The CPR had great plans for its development, as it did for most of the towns along its rail lines. In 1921, an elaborate townsite was surveyed. The community hall, the building of which was begun with volunteer labour early in the 1920's, was located on what was to have been Connaught Street.

But as Burns's poem tells us, "The best laid schemes . . . Gang aft agley." The community hall was both the beginning and the end of urban development in Countess. The grain elevator agent, the CPR section foreman and, for a time, a storekeeper were the only permanent residents it ever attracted.

Socializing by those in the surrounding farming district centred on the hall. In 1923, Countess Community Club had upwards of 30 members, but, as the population dwindled, the hall was sold in 1957 and the community club finally disbanded in 1969.

THE SPRING HILL CANAL SYSTEM

The Rosemary and Duchess areas rely upon the Spring Hill Canal for their water supply. Once filling of the Crawling Valley Reservoir is well advanced,

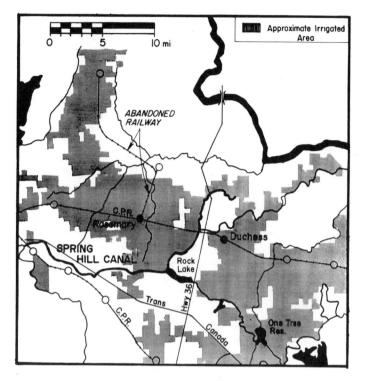

attention will be given to the construction of a canal from the reservoir to the Rosemary area. The canal will irrigate 14,000 acres (6,000 ha) of land transferred from the Spring Hill Canal system which, at present, experiences water deficits in periods of low river flow.

ITS COMMUNITIES

A visitor to the village of Rosemary is immediately struck by the number of large new churches which dominate the scene. These stand as testimony to the various faiths of the settlers who colonized the district. Until recent years the lofty facade of the Roman Catholic church was a familiar landmark in the West Rosemary area. Unfortunately, it has now gone the way of its French Canadian builders and first parishioners, most of whom had left their settlements west of Rosemary, at Clemenceau and East Countess, by the early 1920's.

The three remaining churches are indicators of more permanent settlements of Mennonites, Latter-day Saints and Buddhists. Unlike their French-Canadian predecessors, members of these groups were all experienced farmers — a fact which contributed significantly to their success in irrigation.

The large modern churches of the Mennonites and Latter-day Saints provide places of worship and community gathering spots for the second and third generations who continue to make Rosemary their home.

Although the Japanese Canadians did not come until the 1940's, their adaptation to irrigation farming, coupled with their experience in vegetable growing, has fostered the development of a successful potato-producing industry in the District. The Rosemary Buddhist church is evidence of the Japanese culture and tradition in our midst.

The wide tree-lined main street of Duchess was once bordered with many prosperous businesses. Today, only a fraction of those businesses remain but residential growth in the village and surrounding rural area signals a busy community life.

Growing up at a siding on the CPR's Royal Line, Duchess became a commercial centre. By 1930, it boasted a trading population of 500. Many were irrigation farmers but ranching had long been established in the area north of the village towards the Red Deer River. For the following 20 years, Duchess continued to prosper, and the trading population had grown to over 1,200 by 1950. Soon thereafter, the advent of more efficient — and more expensive — farm machinery led to a consolidation in farm holdings, with a resulting decline in the rural population throughout the EID. Better roads also helped to hasten the loss of both citizens and commerce in Duchess.

Recently, however, the village again experienced a significant population increase when the local oil and gas industry began to provide new jobs. With the local population rising, and the demise of small rural schools, school enrollment has increased tremendously, necessitating the construction of a large addition to the existing school building.

In the winter months, the local hockey arena provides recreation for both youngsters and their parents. Through a strong Agricultural Society, the community has raised sufficient funds, matched by government grants, to improve

Pivot sprinkling from Spring Hill turnout.

arena facilities and construct a spacious new community hall. With its attached kitchen facilities, the meeting hall is used regularly for gatherings of all sorts and the clubrooms upstairs are very popular. Space is also provided for the local library and kindergarten. Along with the four local churches, these modern facilities ensure that Duchess and its environs will continue to maintain a viable community life.

EVOLUTION OF LATHOM FLUME

Structures of this type commonly used in early days of CPR construction. Because of leakage, many were replaced by wood-stave, iron-banded, trestled flumes.

Dismantling Lathom Flume by dragline, 1927.

Work on covered wood-stave flume, 1928. Served until earth-fill replacement canal, photo below, was built in 1972.

Underwood McLellan Ltd.

THE BOW SLOPE CANAL SYSTEM

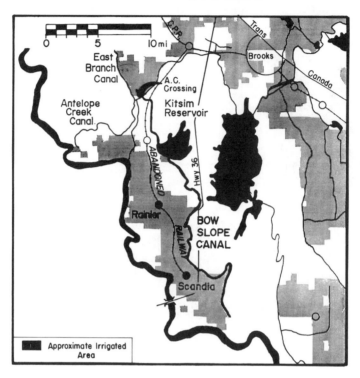

ITS STRUCTURES

The south-western area of the EID is described, by the gentle riverwards curve of its land, as the Bow Slope. Irrigation water is brought to the Bow Slope by way of East Branch Canal. Antelope Creek Canal waters the Bow City area and, beyond the Kitsim Reservoir, the Bow Slope Canal serves the Rainier and Scandia areas.

Water shortages on Rainier and Scandia farms led to the development of the Kitsim Reservoir in 1981. It is filled from the East Branch Canal through the Kitsim Canal.

With an 18,300 acre-foot usable capacity, the reservoir functions as a balancing pond for the Bow Slope part of the irrigation system. It is also the essential supply pond for one of the largest artificially-created wetlands environments in Canada. The Kitsim Project is a joint EID/Ducks Unlimited Canada undertaking to provide nesting habitat for waterfowl.

In naturally-occurring ponds, periodically the water evaporates completely, leaving nesting birds high and dry and contributing to death and disease among them. One of the decisive factors in the successful reproduction of water fowl on the prairie, therefore, is the assurance of reliable water supplies. About 70 basins scattered through the 13,000 -acre (5,200 ha) Kitsim Project provide the guarantee that marshlands will survive the radical climatic extremes of this area.

From the EID Kitsim Reservoir, water is pumped into a gravity-controlled reservoir which was built by DU. Gravity-fed ditches convey the water from this reservoir to the basins.

In addition to providing the reedy marshes favoured by mating geese and ducks, the basins have created much-needed watering holes for stock and spurred the growth of grass on the grazing lands. The Newell Grazing Association has been able to pasture 100 extra cows, with their calves, since the Kitsim Project has been underway.

Ducks Unlimited is now conducting a five-year study to determine how forage crops are affected by the basins. Researchers isolate patches of grass from grazing and measure the annual yields in the test areas. The ultimate aim is to so manage the marshes as to benefit both the birds and the cattle as fully as possible.

Wire cone protects grass at Kitsim from cattle, for DU grazing management study.

ITS COMMUNITIES

In 1907, the region south of the Bow River was opened to homesteaders. Coal was discovered shortly after settlers began to arrive and a seam in the south bank of the Bow was exploited in a small way. Then in 1909, a syndicate of

Montreal and Regina promoters moved in and coal was "king." A townsite covering almost a section of land was laid out; a 40-room hotel, pool hall, dance hall, several stores and a school sprang up and, for a short but heady time, *The Bow City Star* kept its inhabitants abreast of the passing scene. Fairly bursting with confidence, the Board of Trade produced a pamphlet to promote the "Pittsburgh of the North." Talk was buzzing about a network of rail lines that would link Bow City with markets in the United States and, by way of a railway to Churchill on Hudson Bay, with Great Britain and Europe. World War I nipped these grand plans in the pre-bud stage and the city on the Bow never recaptured its initial heights of glory.

A second Bow City arose in the 1930's, not from the ashes of its former incarnation, but on a new site on the north bank of the river. Drylanders had begun to vacate the south side and move onto irrigated farms in the 1920's but the real impetus for the growth of the village came from the development of a strip mining operation, established in 1932. Business prospered and World War II saw the investment of federal funds to enlarge the mine and help to fuel Canada's war effort. Came the 1950's with the move to oil and natural gas for heating, and the fate of the coal industry was, at least temporarily, sealed. The population of Bow City gradually dwindled away.

It may be that yet another rebirth of Bow City is germinating. With growing concern about the finite amounts of petroleum resources, development of coal desposits is once more seriously considered. A seam of sub-bituminous coal near Bow City is estimated to have a reserve of 83 million mineable tons (75 million tonnes). As the overburden is less than 30 feet (9 metres) in depth, exploitation would be economical. Who knows but what in the 1990's, the Pittsburgh of the North will finally become a reality?

Whether irony was intended when the name "Rainier" was chosen is not recorded. The tiny community on the flat, treeless prairie is the namesake of majestic, evergreen-covered Mount Rainier in the state of Washington. It was from this starting point that many of the first settlers migrated to this part of the Bow Slope in 1918.

By strict definition, Rainier and Oasis are separate hamlets but they are so near one another and so interdependent as to be indivisible. Oasis, located on the corner of Highway 36 and the road leading into Rainier, grew up around a restaurant and service station. The restaurant has always been operated by Bow Slope people and, over the years, it has become the "local" where friends and acquaintances gather to exchange news, play cards and take their morning or afternoon break. Bow Slope United Church is nearby.

Within a short driving distance, Rainier proper has a store with a post office, and a community hall. Alcoma School educates children to the secondary level.

Some years ago, an old-time resident of the Bow Slope found himself amassing more horse-drawn farm implements and transportation vehicles than he could possibly accommodate. No true collector lets the small matter of practicality get in the way of his obsession — and Earl Taylor is a true collector. He continued to travel the area, seeking out artifacts that spoke to him of his time and his place.

As he grew older, Taylor began to look for a permanent home for his collection and in 1974, the EID Historical Park was established along the abandoned CPR right-of-way, directly across the street from the Scandia store, post office and service station.

Not only did Mr. Taylor give his collection to the museum, he also donated his life savings to aid in the operation of the park. With the assistance of federal and provincial grants, the EID Historical Park Board, made up of Bow Slope residents, is working to develop a museum park that will reflect the importance of irrigation in forming the character of the EID.

Many of the artifacts were gathered locally. There are fresnoes and scrapers used to build the railroad grade between Scandia and Cassils; a horse-drawn school bus, built on a Ford car running gear and sporting hard rubber tires, ferried Cassils students to the little white school house; a variety of planters and sprayers were used in the potato fields in the early days.

In addition to the caretaker's house, there are other buildings in the park. The plan is to develop these into working models to demonstrate farm techniques from the early days of this century, for the edification of coming generations. One of the more interesting of the outdoor exhibits is a sheep camp, a small portable house trailer that was used on the range in the days when sheep played a vital part in the farmers' livelihood. A barn and a grain elevator will be restored in the future.

One of Mr. Taylor's favourites in the collection is a set of lead-lined cupboard drawers which were originally used to hold foodstuffs in a round-up chuck wagon. A corn chopper is one of the rarest pieces. It is a big, heavy, intricately-geared stationary piece run by the power take-off of a tractor.

The entrance to the park is ringed with a series of monoliths. The face of each large rock is a low-relief, painted sculpture expressing the artist's perception of a particular EID community. Joe Chomistek Sr., from Scandia, executed the pieces. He began to sculpt about 10 years ago and, since then, his art has become his consuming interest. Awareness of Chomistek's work is spreading and commissions are coming in. Ten more of his sculptures will be added to those already in place at the EID Historical Park.

ANTELOPE CREEK WATER CHANNELS

1916. Tarring original concrete siphon to repair leaks.

Tapping the Bow

1921. Banding wood-stave pipe, built to replace concrete structure.

1956. Depicts leakage problems on both structures.

Brooks Studio.

Antelope Creek site today. New spillway, far left, alongside derelict predecessor. Two earlier siphons, right of centre, were replaced by earth-fill crossing in 1960.

THE CASSILS SIPHON

Before the East Branch Canal reaches the Lake Newell inlet, water is taken from it to irrigate the Cassils area.

The village of Cassils included a grain elevator, a blacksmith shop, a hotel and a lumber yard in 1919. It was in that same year that Chris Martin, an American land agent for the CPR, and a Seventh-day Adventist, brought to the Cassils area a large group of his co-religionists. When they met on May 24 to organize the church in their new land, the names of 53 heads of families were recorded. Their little church building, later constructed with volunteer labour, is now located on the grounds of the Brooks and District Museum — one of the few tangible reminders of this once-prospering community.

In 1923, Cassils had a large school, one of the few consolidated school districts in the CPR's Eastern Section. Children were brought to school in Cassils from the outlying districts by horse-drawn school vans, such as the one in the EID Historical Park. Today, the school building is still very much the centre of the community. Renovated as a hall, it is used for family reunions, wedding receptions and office parties. Especially popular in summer, the grounds are grassy and well-shaded.

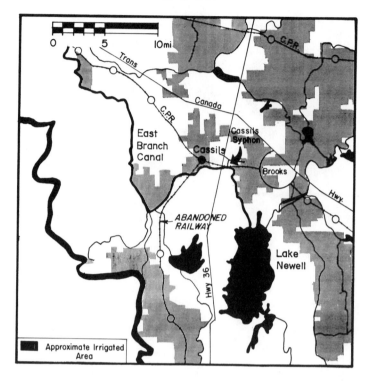

Repairing Cassils Syphon, 1921.

Cassils gained nation-wide exposure when, for a brief two weeks in June of 1973, the spur line from there to Scandia was one of the locations for the filming of *The National Dream*. This made-for-TV movie of Pierre Berton's history of the building of the CPR's trans-continental line used the Cassils locale as a backdrop for scenes of railway construction across the prairies. A dozen or so local residents were hired as extras, as operators of horse-drawn implements or to ensure that the cattle pastured nearby stayed out of camera range. Many friends and neighbours of the "actors" found the filming a fascinating diversion.

Cassils Syphon replacement crossing beneath railway. Built 1978.

THE MAJOR STORAGE RESERVOIR: LAKE NEWELL

F. H. NEWELL

The familiar "Newell", for whom our county and so many of our institutions have been christened, was the director of the United States Reclamation Service during the era of the building of the CPR irrigation project. This Service was a U.S. federal agency staffed by people widely experienced in the development of water delivery systems. They were charged to render fertile those areas of the western states which, without irrigation, would have remained wastelands. The International Congress on Irrigation was organized in 1891 as a forum for the exchange of information on irrigation. The yearly meeting was held in various locales and was regularly attended by representatives of both government and private interests who had a stake in irrigation's future. Presumably, F. H. Newell learned of the CPR project through his acquaintance with J. S. Dennis, Jr., the CPR Superintendent of Irrigation at Calgary. It is certainly possible, given the depth and breadth of Newell's knowledge of irrigation, that his technical advice was solicited by the CPR people. In 1909, Newell carried out a two-week inspection tour of the CPR's irrigation block. At that time, he gave an interview to the *Farm and Ranch Review*, in which he forecast, with impressive accuracy, the future of our area:

> I have just completed a thorough inspection of the irrigation of the Bow River Valley, and there I have found conditions such as to allow the maximum return from the effort of the individual. There is found everything that goes to make a healthy, happy community. You have an adequate water supply, exceptionally good soil for irrigation, rolling country, easily drained, good railroad facilities, your hot summers with their abundance of sunshine will mature the quick ripening crops and your land values have not reached their limit, but will constantly rise as the tract is developed. In fact, I may say that the maximum Western Canada land values, apart from the fruit areas, will ultimately be found in the Bow River Valley irrigated lands.

Newell was the scion of a wealthy Boston family and, together with other moneyed interests from that city, he formed the Boston Newell Company. They purchased half a township in the area west of what was then Crooked Lake (our Lake Newell), running towards Bow City. This was in 1911 before the irrigation system was in operation.

At first glance, it seems curious that Frederick Newell, an avid advocate of irrigation, would become involved in a huge dryland farm. It has been suggested the farm may have been patterned after a common agricultural practice in the United States at that time, the "bonanza" farm. This was a large one-crop farm, cultivated by a force of agricultural labourers. Flax is said to have been grown on the Boston Newell Farm in 1911, but it was hailed out. Large-scale flax farming was practiced in the Bassano area, also, before the arrival of irrigation.

Considering the proximity of the then-booming Bow City and the rush of settlers anticipated when the delivery of water began, it seems likely that Newell's investments were speculative. Hotel Newell was built about 1912 to take advantage of the promised prosperity of Brooks. In the article mentioned above, Newell is quoted as saying:

> Those who acquire these lands are especially fortunate in view of the fact that nowhere else on the continent, possibly in the world, can be secured irrigated land of such fertility and at such a low figure . . .

LAKE NEWELL

The reservoir that bears Newell's name is the largest storage facility in the EID system. It was an important element of Muckleston's original design and its construction took place concurrently with that of Bassano Dam. The reservoir is fed from the north by the East Branch Canal and from the west by the Bow Slope Spillway. Recently, the East Branch Canal was enlarged to improve its delivery capability. When full, Lake Newell stores 176,000 acre-feet of usable water. It carries out the function intended by its designer; that is, it provides the lower part of the system with water. Lake Newell is the largest man-made lake in Alberta. As though by magnetic force, it draws the inhabitants of the surrounding prairie to its shores, and greatly enlivens the leisure hours of a land-locked population.

Still enjoyed today — fishing at Lake Newell Reservoir inlet.   Photographer: H. Pollard.

Cormorant colony at Lake Newell bird sanctuary.

Brooks Bulletin.

Kinbrook Island Provincial Park.

THE ROLLING HILLS CANAL SYSTEM

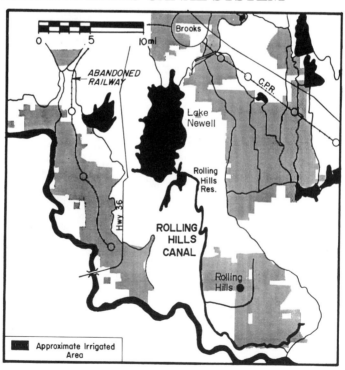

From the 1,350 acre-foot Rolling Hills Reservoir, an adjunct to Lake Newell, the Rolling Hills Canal flows out to irrigate some of the richest land in the EID.

ROLLING HILLS

Rolling Hills is named for a gentle range of hills tumbling away from the reservoir towards the Bow River. Known as "The Banana Belt of the EID," this area is blessed with a warmer climate and a longer frost-free growing period than any other part of the District.

The irrigation ditches were partially laid out by the CPR engineers but the Rolling Hills Canal System was not put into use until 1939, at which late date the area got its first settlers.

Although it was one of the last communities to be settled, Rolling Hills is now, with a population of almost 200, the largest hamlet in the EID. The East Rolling Hills School provides education to the ninth-grade level, and also functions as a meeting facility for numerous clubs and organizations. Other gathering spots for both hamlet and farm residents include the spacious new community hall and adjoining curling rink, and the general store. There, residents can meet their neighbours for a friendly cup of coffee, and do their shopping at the same time. Curling is the sport of choice in winter. The local baseball team enjoys an enthusiastic summer fan club in this recreation-minded and friendly place.

In contrast to the exodus of residents which has characterized many rural communities, Rolling Hills continues to grow. Some of the new residences belong to farm families who have retired to "town." Still other homes are under construction for people moving in from other areas.

Agribusinesses, such as the local alfalfa dehydrating plant and the fertilizer agency, reflect the agricultural base of the community.

THE BROOKS AQUEDUCT

Perhaps the greatest design challenge faced by the CPR engineers, when the irrigation project was on the drawing board, was occasioned by one of the many north-south valleys that score the landscape of the EID. Supply of water to the lower, or eastern, portion of the project depended upon its conveyance from Lake Newell, through the Bantry Canal, and across a valley over 2 miles (3 km) wide and 60 feet (18 metres) deep. The problem was to maintain the flow of water at the desired capacity, while losing as little elevation as possible. The solution was the Brooks Aqueduct, a reinforced-concrete, trestle-supported structure unlike any previously built. Its singularity lay in two particulars: it was the longest aqueduct ever constructed to carry such a large quantity of water, and the first aqueduct in the world to make use of an hydrostatic catenary shape. This means the curve of

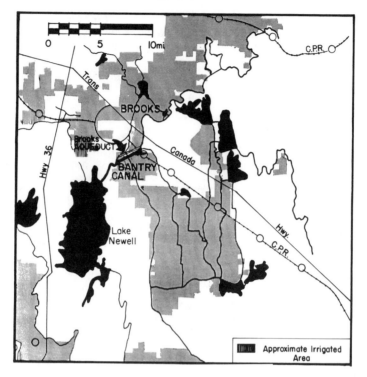

the shell of the flume is formed as though construction material were flexible and capable of adapting its shape to the flow of water through it. An advantage of the design was that under a full load of water, there would be no rotation nor swerve at any point in the shell. In the early 20th century, reinforced concrete was a relatively new building material. Its use in constructing the flume's thin shell was an innovative application. So, too, was its adaptation to the inverted siphon that carried water below ground at the point where the aqueduct crossed the railway line.

From its earliest history, the aqueduct was beset by the problem of water permeating the concrete bowl of the flume. Patching the damaged areas was part of a regular maintenance schedule. The structure did not age well from a functional standpoint and by 1960, the concrete had to be repoured for the entire lower halves of some sections. In the words of R. T. White, a former general manager of the EID, "The aqueduct was an engineer's dream but an operator's nightmare."

In 1973, the federal government, through the offices of the PFRA, agreed to replace the aqueduct with an earth-fill canal. This new structure was ready to go in 1979. It is much more efficient, with a capacity of 950 cfs (27 m³/s) compared with the aqueduct's best of 640 cfs (18 m³/s). Sadly, it is devoid of the charm of its predecessor. Visible for miles from any direction, the aqueduct, darkly etched against the backdrop of the bright prairie sky, was a beautiful piece of classically-proportioned architecture.

For some years, with various organizations and government departments involved, the old aqueduct became something of a political football. It seemed in danger of disappearing completely from our landscape. Luckily, heads with a sense of heritage prevailed. Parks Canada, Alberta Culture and the EID are now negotiating an agreement which will ensure the care and keeping of the remaining 1.5 miles (2.4 km) of the structure. In future, an historical park will be developed, with the Brooks Aqueduct as its focal point, to interpret for tourists the role of irrigation in our society.

Construction on Brooks Aqueduct.

Work gang resting in bowl of aqueduct.

Recently completed aqueduct, 1915.

Ravages of time take toll on concrete. Ongoing repairs to aqueduct.

THE BANTRY CANAL SYSTEMS

The Bantry Canal flows from the north-east edge of Lake Newell into the new earth-fill channel which replaced the old aqueduct.

A little further along, the West Bantry Canal splits off to supply water to Tilley and environs, leaving the main canal to continue on as the North Bantry, responsible for the Patricia and Millicent areas.

THE WEST BANTRY CANAL SYSTEM

ITS STRUCTURES

The West Bantry Canal System is the most complex of all the canal systems in the EID. Land in the eastern portion of the District is generally lower, flatter and heavier than in any other part. This necessitates the use of shorter canals and more reservoirs and drains.

From its inception, Tilley irrigation was hampered by a scarcity of water. The addition of a series of reservoirs has obliterated that problem bit by bit. Cowoki Reservoir was built in 1936. Contracts for its construction were let locally and, for the most part, horses and fresnoes were used in the excavation. One contractor had a D-2 Caterpillar with an earth-moving bucket, a sign of mecha-

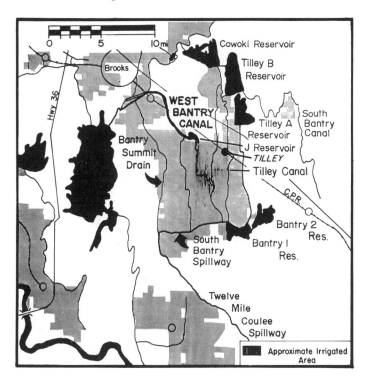

nized times to come. Cowoki was the last dam in the EID to be built under horse power.

Over the years, wherever a natural basin existed that could add to the internal storage capacity, without a large expenditure of capital, it was incorporated into the West Bantry Canal System. Finally, in the early 1970's, the construction of Tilley B Reservoir marked the turning point in the water shortage problems. Ducks Unlimited Canada carried out the building of the original Tilley B Reservoir with funds from the Richard King Mellon Foundation. A later enlargement of the reservoir by the EID was financed by the Alberta Heritage Savings Trust Fund. Storage capacity of the reservoir is now 16,400 acre-feet.

In total, over 24,000 acre-feet are stored in the Tilley-Cowoki reservoir complex. More spillwater is re-used in the West Bantry System than elsewhere in the irrigation complex. Water collected in Tilley A, J Reservoir, Bantry 1 and Bantry 2 is recycled for irrigation.

In the 1984 irrigating season, South Bantry Spillway, constructed to empty into the Twelve Mile Coulee at the lower end of the system, was the site of the first use in the EID of an automated gate. The computerized structure was designed to convey to the water supervisor, by telephone, the status of flow in the spillway. With this knowledge, it was possible to automatically maintain a sufficient level of water to irrigate 4,500 acres (1,800 ha) from the spillway, with two large pumping units. Pleased with the results, engineers at the EID anticipate a future when all main control structures will be automated and orchestrated from a central computer.

Old gate system, built in 1948 in Tilley district.

TILLEY

Much of the land is used to grow alfalfa. For years, the marketing of alfalfa in the EID was done through feeder cattle. Then, a time came in the late 1960's when more alfalfa was raised than the cattle industry demanded. This inspired the founding of an alfalfa dehydrating and cubing plant. The final product, compact

Dragging canal with harrow to control weeds, 1921.

and easier to handle than baled hay, has found excellent export markets. The farmer-owned business has established a relatively stable market for its product and, concomitantly, a reliable outlet for the farmers who grow the hay. A subsidiary company with an almost identical processing plant is now operating in the Rolling Hills area.

The village of Tilley has a population of 358. Tilley's experience in the 1950's was typical of the fate of most villages of that time, and the following picture applies universally to other rural communities of the EID. The advent of fast, reliable vehicles and an even faster, more reliable television button changed the character of the village. Saturday night was no longer the occasion to do shopping, go to the movie and visit with friends over a glass of beer or a cup of coffee. Larger centres beckoned; or else, the household was held at home, mesmerized by the "tube." With the passing of the Saturday-night-on-the-town tradition, the community's social fabric seemed to weaken. This was coincidental with the loss of businesses. Where there had been three general stores, now there was one; the movie house closed; and, soon, the lights on main street went out at 6:00 p.m. every night of the week.

An old prairie adage has it that when the Chinese restaurant shuts down, the demise of the town follows quickly. This happened in Tilley when "Charlie" left. A new beginning was signalled in recent years when the one cafe in Tilley was purchased by a Chinese-Vietnamese family.

Community activities today centre on the 17-room school, the large, well-appointed hall and the new indoor ice arena. The life of the church continues to prosper in Tilley. St. Jude's Roman Catholic Church is the largest denomination; many of its adherents are of Czechoslovakian descent. The Evangelical Free Church is also well attended. Bethany Lutheran Church, seven miles (12 km) south-west of Tilley, serves the Danish community who build their lives around its presence. In the 1960's, young Mennonite families from the Rosemary area settled on farms near Tilley. Their community has grown to the point where children attend a private religious school.

Tapping the Bow

THE NORTH BANTRY CANAL SYSTEM

ITS COMMUNITIES

Following the North Bantry branch of the Bantry Canal System leads us to the Princess-Patricia-Millicent area. The rail line that runs through these communities now sees very occasional freight traffic, but it has a "royal" history. At one time, it was a busy communications artery connecting Bassano with Swift Current, Saskatchewan. It was called the "Royal Line" and many of the settlements along its length were correspondingly named: Bassano for an Italian nobleman; Rosemary, Duchess, Patricia and Millicent for the female members of the Duke of Sutherland's family; the generic Countess, Princess and Empress were thrown in for good aristrocratic measure.

Although it has a population of about 20 people, Princess is not a hamlet by governmental definition. This is because all of its homes are company-owned, provided for the employees of the nearby compressor station.

An explosion at the plant in 1980 put Princess on the national map. Huge tongues of fire licking the darkening evening sky could be seen from miles around. Fortunately, no human tragedy resulted from the accident, and the plant has since been completely rebuilt.

The EID supplies all of the water used in Princess. It is stored in two 6-million-gallon (22.7-million-litre) reservoirs which are filled in irrigating season from the North Bantry System. This supply serves the needs of the compressor station and the households; as well, it is used by a 2-acre (0.8 ha) greenhouse operation.

Like many of the small settlements of the EID, Patricia and Millicent were much busier places in the early half of this century than they are today. In those years, they served as major shopping centres for the farms in their environs, as well as for the ranching interests north of the Red Deer River.

Now, Patricia is best known for its annual Labour Day rodeo, which draws attendance from far afield. Professional chuckwagon races are a major attraction of the two-day event.

Farming is carried on in the area, but the heart of Patricia beats most strongly to the rhythms of horses and cattle and grasslands. The hamlet's personality is expressed by its "watering hole," a rustic bar and restaurant in the local hotel where the washrooms are designated for "Mares" and "Studs."

The Imperial Colony lies north of Patricia. Its name is in keeping with the "royal" flavour. Land in the colony went on sale in 1920. Although the farms were not sold under the Veterans' Land Act, a number of the first settlers were returned soldiers from World War I.

12-horse team used in canal construction, 1920's.

CPR VIPs visit construction camp at Patricia, 1919.

Break in "Nigger John Flume", 1929. Built to divert water to Imperial Colony from Spring Hill Canal. In 1970, present earth-fill was built.

An initial wave of settlement quickly ebbed. The structure built to convey irrigation water to the area proved to be inadequate. This fact, made more trying by a disastrous crop year in 1921, drove the newcomers off the land.

Although times were tough on irrigated farms, they were much worse on dryland north of the Red Deer. Migration southwards took place in the latter 1920's. It was this that settled the Imperial Colony and added to the rural population in the Patricia and Millicent areas. Descendants of many of the families who came at that time have remained.

Of the several colonies settled by the CPR between 1914 and 1930, the Imperial Colony is the only one still to use the designation "colony."

Haddington School in Patricia serves the entire surrounding area, with instruction as far as the sixth grade. Older students are bused to Duchess for secondary education. When schools were centralized, the Imperial Colony retained its small schoolhouse as a gathering place.

Millicent is Uncle Tom's Cabin Store. Tom Charlton is much more than the proprietor of the store — he is a local institution. His family has been in business in Millicent since 1915 when they opened a hotel and livery stable.

From early morning until late evening, Tom, with the help of his wife, Laura, operates the store seven days a week, 52 weeks a year, with one exception — Christmas Day. It's an old-fashioned country store, with every imaginable commodity stocking its shelves. Customers come for their supplies, but they inevitably stay to enjoy some of the side-benefits — a rousing political debate or a pithy assessment of our life and times from the man behind the counter.

Tom's give-away pens are inscribed, "Uncle Tom's Cabin Store on the Way to Dinosaur Park." Dinosaur Provincial Park is located in the furthest north-east corner of the EID, on the banks of the Red Deer River. The park may be one of the richest, undeveloped natural resources of the area. Its large potential to foster tourism is only now being realized. The park's many facets are fully discussed further along in this book, in the section devoted to the recreational attractions of the EID.

Because it lies beyond the distribution points of the canal system along which our imaginary tour of the EID was conducted, Dinosaur Provincial Park receives only spillwater from the irrigation system. It is collected in Little Sand Hill Creek, which flows through the campground of the park, and in the larger drainage channel, One Tree Creek, which dumps into the Red Deer River a little further upstream.

Dinosaur Provincial Park.

Kids splashing in Little Sand Hill Creek.

By travelling from Bassano Dam, through the various canal chains and, eventually, into one of the major drainage networks, we have followed the course of the water full circle — from its intake to the point where unused portions are returned to the South Saskatchewan River system, to which both the Bow and the Red Deer Rivers belong.

To some, the irrigation system may seem "as common as ditch water," to take license with an old simile. Seen as a number of smaller systems, each separate, yet attuned to the larger system, it has the beauty of a well-oiled mechanism in which the parts operate smoothly and efficiently to do the job assigned them.

AN EID PHOTO ALBUM

Begun as free-style contest, Gem Rodeo ran yearly from 1917-1968.

Courtesy, J. P. Royer.

Dipping vat used to treat cattle for mange.

Glenbow Archives.

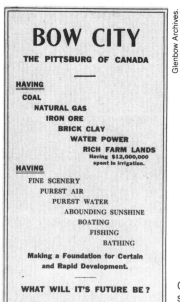

Glenbow Archives.

BOW CITY

THE PITTSBURG OF CANADA

HAVING

COAL
    NATURAL GAS
        IRON ORE
           BRICK CLAY
               WATER POWER
                  RICH FARM LANDS
                    Having $12,000,000
                    spent in irrigation.

HAVING

  FINE SCENERY
    PUREST AIR
      PUREST WATER
        ABOUNDING SUNSHINE
          BOATING
            FISHING
              BATHING

Making a Foundation for Certain and Rapid Development.

WHAT WILL IT'S FUTURE BE?

Glenbow Archives.

Blackfoot at Bassano celebration, July 1, 1924. Photographer: R. A. Bird.

Cover of promotional pamphlet issued by Prairie Coal Company, Regina.

Quilt showing Alberta brands registered in 1880's.

John Ware ranch, located north of Millicent in 1902.

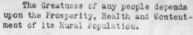

BE GREAT, THEREFOR BE AN IRRIGATOR.

The Greatness of any people depends upon the Prosperity, Health and Contentment of its Rural Population.

Irrigation creates Prosperity from Water, Sunshine and Soil.

Happiness creates Health; Health Contentment and Contentment
Greatness. To be Great be an Irrigator.

Attend the Bassano Irrigation Convention. Novr. 23, 24 & 25 and hear what experienced irrigators have to say. You will be welcome.
        John S. MAVOR, Chairman
        R. A. TRAVIS, Secy.
        Board of Control.

Lethbridge Northern Irrigation District.

Postcard to advertise irrigation convention held in Bassano, 1915.

A CPR vice-president visits. Duchess railway station, 1920.

Courtesy, Mr. and Mrs. P. J. Penner.

Clemenceau School, west of Rosemary.   Artist: S. Dyck.

Irrigating a pea field, 1938.

Crowd at first Bassano train station, 1910.

Bounty of vegetables grown in EID.

Courtesy, S. Alberts.

German prisoners-of-war working in potato field — One Tree district. 1940's.

Brooks Studio.

"Products of Rainier" charm parade on-lookers.

Irrigation Farming is Successful Farming Because It is Business Farming

Checking the check.

Glenbow Archives.

Peas and corn were canned in this facility from late 1940's to 1960's.

Buckerfield's alfalfa de-hydrating plant. Brooks, 1950.

J. L. Carroll Photographics Ltd.

J. L. Carroll Photographics Ltd.

Prior to opening of this facility in 1946, milk was shipped from Brooks to Bassano for processing.

Knight and Watson sheep farm on Bow Slope, 1920.

Brand new school van, 1948.

Recess is for climbing trees.

Music draws EID communities together.

Retirement home for senior citizens.

Brooks Studio.

Brooks Bulletin.

Brooks and District Museum grounds, 1979.

The lives of countless EID young people have been enriched through 4-H activities.
Photographer: S. Alberts.

J. L. Carroll Photographics Ltd.

4-H calf show in Evergreen Park, 1947.

Brooks Bulletin.

Chow line at Newell Grazing Association round-up.

Community Cultural Centre served earlier as Brooks hospital.

Brooks Bulletin.

Newell County Art Club show,
Cassils Centre Mall.

Brooks Bulletin.

Courtesy, J. Ferguson.

Baseball was popular in EID until 1950's. Patricia Oilers, league champs 1939-49, Intermediate Baseball Champs 1941.

Courtesy, J. Robertson.

Elaborate float design by Alta Crook, wife of long-time EID district engineer.

Start of Alberta Wheat Pool elevator, Rainier siding, 1927.

Grain elevator — architectural prairie landmark.

Brooks Bulletin.

Mining coal east of Brooks in 1930's.

Patricia Main Street, 1960's.   Photographer: S. Alberts.

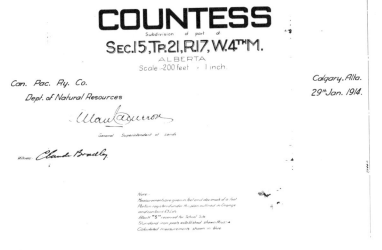

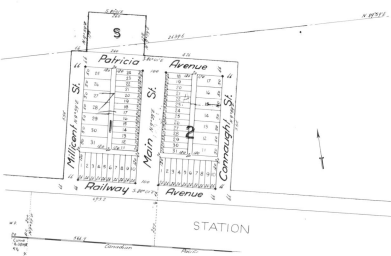

CPR had such grand plans as this for most railway sidings. Photographer: K. Kimura.

Chuckwagon races at Patricia rodeo.

Artist Joe Chomistek, Sr. at opening of EID Historical park.

No rain on the annual Farmers' Day parade.

Drilling rig. Single-stand derrick, joints of drill stem on racks in foreground.

Brooks Bulletin.

CPR barn at Matoka ditchrider reservation, 1923.

Wooden sidewalks along 2nd Avenue, Brooks.

Subdivisions spring up in 1970's boom.

Truss replaces spans washed out of highway bridge that once crossed the Bow below Bassano Dam, 1916.

First Brooks swimming pool, 1930.

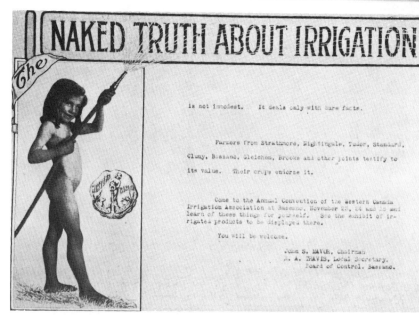

Western Canada Irrigation Association promotional literature, 1915.

J. L. Carroll Photographics Ltd.

Rosemary under water. April 1948 flood.

Courtesy, J. Walde.

Burning the 10-year mortgage in 1974. Gem's was one of first natural gas co-ops formed in Alberta.

Rolling Hills parade entry.

Brooks Studio.

Oil tank cars at Princess siding.

Courtesy, E. Lapp.

Photographer: S. Alberts.

Brooks in 1945.

Brooks Bulletin.

Brooks in depths of winter.

Brooks and District Museum.

Brooks Bulletin.

Main Street, Tilley. Left, in 1915. Below, in 1964.

Fair at Bassano CPR headquarters, 1919.

Moving Princess ditchrider house to Patricia, 1931.

BROOKS: THE HUB OF THE DISTRICT

Brooks is the geographical, administrative, commercial and cultural centre around which the life of the District ebbs and flows. At the entrance to the town, a large welcome sign informs us that we are "Where Water Works Wonders." The tree-lined streets, numerous parks, and well-kept lawns and gardens reflect some of the benefits of irrigation that cannot be measured in dollars and cents. The basic human urge to beautify our surroundings would be squelched were it not for the availability of water.

Beginning as a set of corrals and a loading chute beside the CPR main line, Brooks owes its start to the ranching industry. Drawn by tales of the tall and plentiful grass, ranchers arrived in the latter days of the last century, driving cattle and horses overland or shipping them in by rail. This was the "last, best West" — with the emphasis on "last."

With commencement of construction on the irrigation system in 1910, a new era began for Brooks. On the one hand, that event proved to be the beginning of the end of the open range; and on the other, it signalled a time of explosive population growth for the town. The huge work gangs who constructed the aqueduct and canal systems had big dollars to spend, and homestead lands had just been opened up in the districts surrounding the irrigation block. What a bonanza for local merchants! New establishments sprang up, virtually overnight, to provide food, lodgings, agricultural machinery and other services.

E. O. (Bert) Coultis organized the first newspaper in the village. Published for a few months in 1910, it was a Board of Trade advertising sheet. Later that same year, Calvin Goss, an American printer and newspaper man, established the weekly *Brooks Banner*. Its pages waxed enthusiastic about the great future in store. The August 18, 1910 issue boasted that, within ten years,

> Brooks will be a city of from three to ten thousand people and the prairies on every side will be divided up into small irrigated farms, where beautiful crops of fruits and grains will be grown and where one may rest in the shade of trees . . .

If things had gone on booming, Mr. Goss might have been proved right. Unfortunately, the first world war slowed things up, and then, there were a few dry years for the homesteaders. The locating of the CPR administrative offices and staff residences at Brooks really gave the town a boost, but when the bottom fell out of the market for agricultural products in the 1920's — well, it took a lot longer than ten years for the population to reach the 3,000 mark.

Providing commercial and community services for the surrounding farming population continued to be the town's major role for the next decade or so. On July 6, 1935, *The Calgary Herald* printed a feature story, "Brooks Centre of Huge Enterprise: New Era Opens for Irrigated District With Farm Control." The town and district were described, both in their historical context and in their current state. It was said that,

> Brooks is an attractive and modern town, with a population of 750. It has many charming homes and numerous substantial business places . . . In the matter of modern facilities, Brooks lacks nothing of the essentials.

The local merchants of the day were said to be generally optimistic about the future; they expected that the large reduction in land prices, effected by the newly-formed EID, would not only benefit present contract holders, but would also attract new settlers to the area. Business was bound to increase.

Only gradually did the predicted growth occur. The next 30 years were characterized by steady progress. Finally, the long-predicted boom took place in the latter half of the 1970's — brought on, this time, not by the agricultural industry, but by the oil business.

Although activity had been stepped up in the early 1960's, the oil and gas industry did not really come into its own until increased demand for natural gas, and the accompanying price hike, spurred exploration and development of the shallow gas fields underlying most of this part of the province. Between 1970 and 1975, the Brooks population swelled from 3,900 to 5,600. By the end of the decade, the influx of personnel to staff the burgeoning exploration, development and service sectors of "the oil patch" had shot the population figure up over the 9,000 mark. New subdivisions were built. A large industrial park was developed, and the library, town office and fire hall facilities were all replaced. During this time, too, new hospitals and schools were constructed, and the Alberta Government Service Centre was built to house a rapidly-expanding civil service. Although the most recent economic slowdown has brought a brief lull in the boom, Brooks continues to play its vital role of service centre to the agricultural and petroleum industries.

In addition to catering to the commercial aspects of life, Brooks functions, also, as the cultural centre for the District. For those who wish to glimpse into our past, the Brooks and District RCMP Century Museum, located on the northeast side of town, provides an interesting and informative experience. Since its inception in 1975, the museum's acquisitions have included: a life-size model of a duck-billed dinosaur; the Duchess railway station; the Alberts house, built by the CPR to house an engineer, and later moved to the One Tree district; Parvella, a Northwest Mounted Police post, built in the early 1900's and moved from its original site north of the Red Deer; and an ever-expanding array of photographs, artifacts, and household, farm and oilfield equipment from our past.

The Brooks Recreation Centre provides facilities for many sports activities: hockey, ice skating, curling, swimming and diving may be enjoyed there. Always a sports-minded place, Brooks also has baseball diamonds, tennis courts and children's playgrounds aplenty to meet the recreational needs of the town and District. Other types of recreational opportunities are provided through Brooks Community Band, the Handicraft Guild and Brooks Public Library. The newly-completed amphitheatre at Griffin Park School is one of the busiest spots in town. Its full range of stage and sound equipment make it ideal for musical and theatrical events. Another very busy place is the Community Cultural Centre which houses, among many other community facilities, the Brooks Campus of Medicine Hat College. The recent addition of this post-secondary institution served to round out the educational opportunities already available through Brooks School District and Brooks Further Education Council.

One community service program, unique to Brooks, provides an opportunity for adult volunteers to be matched with young people; its objectives are companionship, a listening ear and just plain fun. Aptly titled Special People Enjoying Children (SPEC), this service was developed within the community by local citizens to meet local needs. Its great success is testimony to the dedication and support of its staff, clients, volunteers, board members and the community-at-large.

Other important elements in the overall community health care system include a modern hospital complex, consisting of ambulance service, mental health and public health clinics, general and auxiliary hospitals, and a nursing home; medical, dental and chiropractic clinics; senior citizens' lodge and apartment buildings; and the district offices of Alberta Social Services and Community Health, and Alberta Alcoholism and Drug Abuse Commission.

Government services, both provincial and federal, are dominated by those related to the local agricultural base: Alberta Agriculture's district office — district agriculturalists, district home economist, irrigation specialists — and the Alberta Horticultural Research Centre; and Agriculture Canada's veterinarian, Farm Credit Corporation, Farm Labour Pool and Fresh Water Fish Marketing Corporation.

A full range of legal and accounting services, financial institutions, service clubs, community organizations, and churches round out the community profile.

And, to keep us all in touch with one another, and with the rest of the world, we have an effective communications network. Remember the old *Brooks Banner?* Well, in 1912, the proprietorship was taken over by one Leonard D. Nesbitt, who subsequently changed the name to *The Brooks Bulletin*. Now, more than 70 years later, *The Bulletin* is printed and edited by two of the elder Nesbitt's grandsons. Their father is the publisher. Alberta's largest weekly, which "covers the EID like the noonday sun," is an eagerly-awaited Wednesday event. Its high standards of community news coverage are recognized by its avid readers, as well as by the Alberta Weekly Newspaper Association.

The electronic media is represented by CIBQ, the local radio station, which operates 24 hours daily, keeping its listeners in touch with local news, sports and weather, and the latest in country music releases.

The Brooks of today, like that of 50 years past, continues to be "the business centre of a wide area of irrigated farming country and in itself a living testimony of the richest natural beauty attainable through a plentiful use of water." Although Mr. Goss's long-ago prediction of 10,000 inhabitants has yet to materialize, the Brooks of 1985 is a far cry from that brand-new village of 75 years past.

ORGANIZATION OF THE EID

The creation of agricultural bounty, brought about by the application of sufficient irrigation water, is the major responsibility of the organization known as the Eastern Irrigation District. Part landowner, part co-operative, part large corporation in the business of building and maintaining a huge system of structures, reservoirs, canals and drainage ditches, the EID has played a leading role in shaping the Brooks community, as well as the larger community of the surrounding farming district.

Graced by towering trees planted when the irrigation project was in its infancy, Evergreen Park in the downtown core of Brooks, is the setting for the attractive red-brick headquarters building from which the activities of the EID are co-ordinated. Built in 1979 to replace the original CPR building, its predominant colours are warm, earthy tones of orange, brown and green, carrying the hues of our agricultural setting indoors. Evergreen Park was originally designated as a picnicking spot for farm families. Today, its facilities have been expanded to cater to physical fitness buffs, through the Participark.

EID Board of Directors and General Manager at opening of present EID office building, 1979.

Because its water assessment rolls show in excess of 200,000 irrigable acres (90,000 ha), the Irrigation Act of Alberta specifies that a board of seven directors are to be chosen in the EID, each to serve a three-year term. Although voting is done on a District-wide basis, one director is elected to represent each of the seven electoral districts into which the EID is divided. The terms of office are staggered in order to provide continuity of board membership, with two board positions coming up for election each year. Before beginning each year's business, the directors choose a chairman from among their number.

Original headquarters, built by CPR in 1915.

Giant white spruce line entrance to Evergreen Park.

Brooks Bulletin.

To oversee the complex activities of the organization, the EID Board of Directors then hires a general manager, to whom report the five departmental managers. The titles of these departments reflect the major areas of activity entailed in running the large corporation: Administration, Engineering, Equipment, Grazing Leases, and Operation and Maintenance.

The EID's large landholdings mean that the staff functions are different from those in other irrigation districts in the province. The required number of staff is much greater than for most irrigated areas.

Because of the sheer physical size of the irrigation system and the fact that "carrier" canals must sometimes traverse distances as great as 25 miles (40 km) across the prairie to link pockets of irrigated land, the Operations and Maintenance division has a large staff complement. A fleet of vehicles is maintained to convey workers and supervisors to work sites around the District. The EID also possesses a large number of earth-moving machines for construction and maintenance of canals, reservoirs, etc.

The most noticeable difference in the EID's operations, however, is related to the large tracts of grasslands that it owns and administers. On this land are located hundreds of oil and gas wells, for which the petroleum companies pay compensation to the landowner. In 1983, an income over $2 million from surface rights and right-of-way leases was contributed to the District's general revenues. With this extra revenue come attendant costs in administration.

In addition to providing the oil and gas industry with sites on which to locate their production, storage, transmission and processing facilities, these vast areas of uninhabited prairie serve an extremely important agricultural purpose. They furnish pasture for more than 25,000 cow-calf units belonging to the water users. This grassland resource has been instrumental in the region's livestock economy ever since the days of the open range.

Reception area, EID office building.
Photographer: K. Kimura.

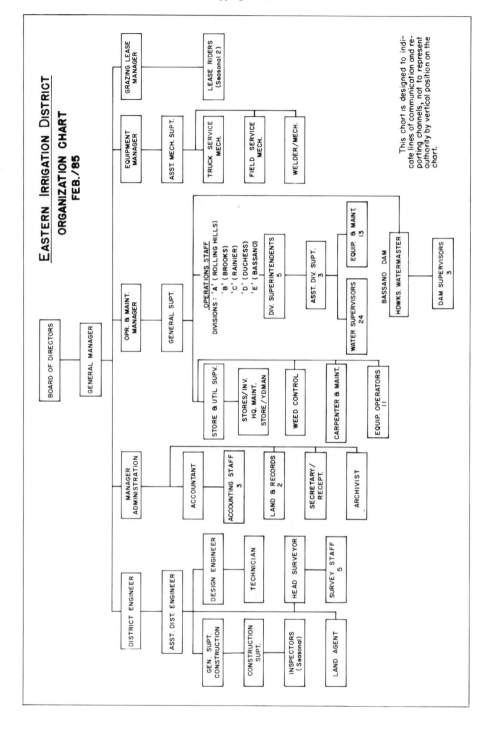

EASTERN IRRIGATION DISTRICT
ORGANIZATION CHART
FEB./85

This chart is designed to indicate lines of communication and reporting channels, not to represent authority by vertical position on the chart.

Administrative staff.

Preparing construction plans.

Stores staff.

Studying canal drawing.

Selecting design elements.

Welding in pre-cast shop.

Vehicle service bay.

All photographs by K. Kimura.

Computer age accounting.

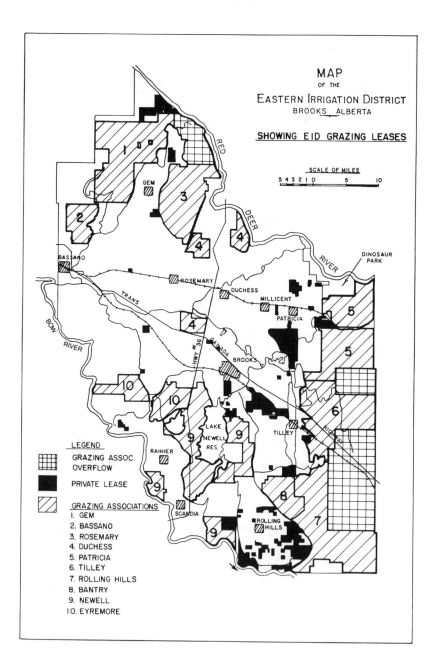

MAP
OF THE
EASTERN IRRIGATION DISTRICT
BROOKS ALBERTA

SHOWING EID GRAZING LEASES

SCALE OF MILES
5 4 3 2 1 0   5   10

LEGEND

GRAZING ASSOC. OVERFLOW

PRIVATE LEASE

GRAZING ASSOCIATIONS
1. GEM
2. BASSANO
3. ROSEMARY
4. DUCHESS
5. PATRICIA
6. TILLEY
7. ROLLING HILLS
8. BANTRY
9. NEWELL
10. EYREMORE

GRAZING LEASES

When the CPR developed the Eastern Section of its irrigation project, over 1,000,000 acres (405,000 ha) of native grassland were available for grazing. The railway company was guaranteed a tax-exempt period of 24 years on all lands granted it for building the main line. As long as the grazing land within the irrigation block was not taxed, the CPR cast a lenient eye on its use. However, when "wild lands" taxes were levied in the late 1920's, the CPR sought to recover this cost by leasing the land.

The Alberta government enacted legislation to assure residents of the irrigation block first opportunity to the leases. Demand from those local farmers in a financial position to apply for leases was soon met. The CPR then leased the remaining grazing lands to non-resident ranchers who had traditionally used the range. Many of these latter leases were long-term.

The depression of the Thirties lowered prices to the extent that it was not economically feasible to raise cattle in irrigated areas; as a result, many leases were cancelled. In 1935, the newly-formed Eastern Irrigation District gained title to this large area of grassland and, with it, the onus of paying local taxes. Later that same year, unleased lands became a double liability when the taxes were drastically increased. The board of trustees felt that the grasslands were taxed at an exhorbitant rate; and, as their limited budget could not handle such an increase in expenditures, they decided to sell off a large portion. Over 400,000 acres (162,000 ha) were bought by the few local farmers and ranchers who were beginning to build up larger cattle herds and, consequently, needed more year-round grazing land.

In the aftermath of the Depression, the 10- and 21-year leases, originally made by the CPR, began to expire. The board decided not to renew those of non-residents; instead, the pasture lands were reserved for local farmers and ranchers. Over the previous decade, cattle prices had been rising. This upward trend, coupled with the availability of extra feed grain produced in the irrigated areas, convinced more and more farmers that livestock production would provide a much-needed source of income.

About that same time, in an effort to obtain more information about the operation of their irrigation district, water users in 13 different locales selected representatives, called "contact men." These individuals met with the board two or three times a year to discuss District affairs. They were the connecting link between the board of trustees and the water users. This two-way communication proved extremely valuable — especially in the formation of community pastures, or grazing associations.

Aided by the efforts of their contact men, groups of water users, who lived close enough together to share leases, began to approach the board to have summer pasture made available to them on a joint rental basis. Because of good relations between the trustees and the contact men, these requests were granted. This process of reserving large grassland areas for community leases began about 1941. The first grazing association in the EID was formed at Rosemary in 1942, followed by the Tilley-Rolling Hills group in 1945. Between 1947 and 1949, community pastures were established for Countess, Newell, Patricia, Gem and Bassano. The process continued into the 1950's with the establishment of the Duchess, Eyremore and Bantry leases.

At the present time, there are still about 57,000 acres (23,068 ha) of grassland leased year-round to individual farmers and ranchers of the District. These parcels are scattered throughout the EID and cannot be conveniently annexed to community leases.

The grazing associations are registered under the Societies Act of Alberta. Each must elect a board of directors, hold an annual meeting and otherwise abide by the terms of this statute. The grazing association appoints or hires a range manager who is responsible for carrying out the regulations of the local community lease. Most associations also employ a lease rider to ensure the health and safety of their cattle. The association employees work closely with the EID's grazing lease manager. The overall administration of the 600,000 acres (242,820 ha) of grazing lands in the District is his responsibility.

Community leases serve the needs of the many local irrigation farmers who require summer range for their cattle; they operate from May 1 through October 31 of each year. Farmers are discouraged from maintaining larger herds than can be cared for on their own farms over the winter months. Any qualified water user may apply to the board of directors of a grazing association for membership. In case of disputes arising over admission, or any other policy of the grazing association, the EID's board of directors is the final authority.

Rental rates for leases have been established so that a portion of the total revenue from grazing lands goes toward taxes and administration costs, while the remainder is applied to general revenues. This procedure benefits the local farmers in two ways: one, the rental rates for community leases are kept at a reasonable level; and two, all water users in the District receive a subsidy for their water rates.

Carrying capacities of the grazing lands may be increased when ground moisture, built up from irrigation seepage or from man-made lakes and reservoirs, results in richer grass cover and more stock watering holes. Ducks Unlimited Canada has co-operated with the EID, since the early 1940's, to develop projects that use dams and other structures to catch water from the irrigation system. Many acres of grasslands, formerly of limited grazing value, have been improved by this conservation program; and both waterfowl and livestock benefit.

Regrassing is another method used to upgrade the efficiency of grazing leases. This is the process of breaking up the sod and seeding the prepared bed with tame grasses and legumes. The EID began a regrassing program in the 1960's; every year since 1969, about 31,000 acres (12,546 ha) of grassland have been improved in this way. Regrassing doubles the number of cattle the land can support in its native state. The carrying capacity of community pastures in the District today is 22,000 cow-calf units.

At present, the EID is studying grazing lease policy to determine whether the best possible use is being made of its grasslands. Preliminary investigation shows that applying irrigation to these lands would greatly increase carrying capacity. Where now a cow-calf unit requires 27 acres (11 ha) of grazing land, the same unit could be supported by only 2 acres (0.8 ha) of irrigated pasture. Concurrently with this study, the board of directors is analysing the impact of the District's cattle industry. They want to ascertain whether the added costs connected with irrigating community pastures could be justified by the economic benefits of increased beef production.

WHY WE IRRIGATE

CLIMATE

Several factors are involved in determining whether an area will benefit from irrigation. First and foremost among these, of course, is climate. If one word could be used to sum up the climatic conditions of the EID, that word would be "dry." Average annual precipitation is less than 13 inches (330 mm). In the good years, heavy snowfalls blanket the winter landscapes; spring thaw is gradual and, as the snow melts, moisture is released into the earth, providing an ideal medium for seed germination. Gentle rains nurture the crops through to maturity and harvest is taken in through the dry, golden days of autumn.

But, as any farmer will testify, Nature is not consistently benevolent. Variability in the timing, as well as in the amount, of precipitation is a fact of life on the prairies of southeastern Alberta. Evaporation intensifies the effects of limited precipitation on agriculture.

High summer temperatures (in the mid-thirty-degree-Celsius range) are often accompanied by hot drying winds, causing an annual moisture deficit of 8 inches (200 mm). Wind is a factor in winter, too. The Chinook, a warm westerly, blows down from the Rocky Mountains at speeds of up to 60 miles (100 km) per hour. In its gusts, temperatures spike. It is not uncommon for the mercury to shoot up, in a matter of hours, from 40° below zero Fahrenheit (− 40°C) to well above the freezing mark. Snows melt rapidly under the Chinook's balmy breath. While the sound of water dripping from the roof may lift the hearts of the dwelling's inhabitants who have been suffering through a prolonged period of deep and unrelenting cold, the earth is less receptive. In its frozen state, it is unable to absorb the moisture from the thaw, and much of it is lost to run-off.

Temperature variations in this area can also be extreme — both from year-to-year at the same location, and between different locations within the District. South of Brooks, the climate is similar to that of Lethbridge and Taber, especially in the Rolling Hills and Scandia areas, which are close to the Bow River. As one moves north of Brooks, the climate becomes more like that of the Hanna-Stettler regions, in that there is more precipitation and a shorter growing season.

Radical temperature differences between various points in the District are commonplace. The story is told of two farmers who met in Brooks on a winter day in the early 1960's. One fellow was from Rolling Hills, the "banana belt of the EID." He was delighted by the Chinook blowing over his place; temperatures were in the 60-degree-Fahrenheit range (15°C), and he had done his morning chores in his shirt sleeves. In contrast, his fellow water user from north of Duchess cursed the 15°-below-zero-Fahrenheit (− 25°C) reading at his home. In order to get *his* cattle fed before coming to town, he'd had to don his long johns and bundle up, jamming his cap down over his ears. Then the *!!*!!*!! tractor would hardly turn over . . . such are the vagaries of temperature in the EID!

The minimum temperature of 56° below zero Fahrenheit (− 49°C) was registered at Brooks one crackling crisp night in 1924; the record high occurred in the summer of 1919, when the mercury skyrocketed to 104° Fahrenheit (40°C).

Where the Sun Shines ... Crops Flourish

Hours of Sunshine During Growing Season

Year	May	June	July	August	September	Total	Year
1926	280.2	321.8	356.5	250.4	145.4	1,354.3	1926
1927	161.4	289.5	354.6	292.5	196.8	1,294.8	1927
1928	334.0	230.2	329.9	306.6	241.1	1,431.8	1928
1929	249.8	270.2	385.7	352.8	170.0	1,428.5	1929
1930	244.8	272.2	358.7		Not available		1930
1931	225.8	242.0	308.2	299.0	145.6	1,220.6	1931
1932	210.3	212.4	322.4	281.4	212.6	1,239.1	1932
1933	225.4	308.2	359.2	284.4	182.6	1,359.8	1933
1934	215.9	242.2	349.5	308.9	141.6	1,258.1	1934
1935	217.7	223.2	341.7	288.2	205.8	1,276.6	1935
1936	297.4	257.8	361.5	259.0	197.5	1,373.2	1936
1937	264.0	264.9	301.8	287.7	178.7	1,297.1	1937
1938	192.9	231.2	324.2	296.5	239.5	1,314.3	1938
1939	246.5	211.3	344.6	307.1	197.4	1,306.9	1939
1940	269.3	309.9	267.9	340.2	200.6	1,587.9	1940
Average	242.3	258.5	337.7	276.9	179.0		

Average per growing season (14 years) ....1,328.8 hours

Average per day (growing season, 14 years).. 8.6 hours

Long Frost-Free Period

Temperatures for the years 1926 to 1940 for the growing season (April-September, both months inclusive):

	April	May	June	July	August	September
Maximum mean	55.8°	67.3°	74.8°	82.8°	78.9°	66.7°
Minimum mean	27.9°	39.6°	47.6°	52.8°	48.8°	38.8°

Killing Frost-Free Period (15-year average)—139.2 days.
   This compares favourably with similar areas in the prairie provinces.

Wind velocity, May-September period (15-year average)—8.5 M.P.H.

Similar mind-boggling extremes occur in the length of the growing season, defined as the number of consecutive days each year when the temperature remains above − 1.6 degrees Celsius. The sixty-one-year average is 136 days. Farmers in 1921 were brought up short at 96 days, while their counterparts nineteen years later, in 1940, luxuriated in a full 180 days in which to grow their crops.

In the past, intermittent wet cycles tended to obscure the essential nature of the southern Alberta climate. When the land blossomed under the blessing of rain, dryland farming was an appealing proposition to homesteaders and land developers. But, in the longer spells of drought, hard lessons were learned. Although average annual precipitation is about 13 inches (330 mm), records kept in Brooks since 1916 show variations from a low of 7 inches (178 mm) in 1918 to a high of 23.3 inches (591 mm) in 1951.

A stable, intensive agricultural base is not built on averages. To rely solely upon the timely arrival of moisture in a region of extreme climatic variability is to increase the element of chance in an already risky business. The twin climatic features of low precipitation and high evaporation losses are the main factors dictating the necessity for irrigation in this region.

What southern Alberta lacks in humidity, however, it makes up for in sunlight. The sun shines an average of eight hours daily from the beginning of May to the end of September. The benefits of irrigation, combined with the favorable climate, allow for the cultivation of a wide variety of agricultural commodities.

SOILS

When determining the suitability for irrigation of any area, soil type is also an important consideration. In order for irrigation to be effective, the soil must be well-drained and fertile enough to support the increased crop yields that are necessary to repay the large capital and labour investments that irrigation requires.

Soils in the EID vary considerably, from silty loams to heavier clay loams, all grouped under the general classification of brown soil. For the most part, they are characterized by good drainage and have proved wonderfully productive with the application of water. The soils of southern Alberta are, by and large, of glacial origin. They were formed when immense sheets of ice ground out across the prairies during the Ice Age, pulverizing boulders and bedrock. When the great thaw began, about 18,000 years ago, the withdrawal of the ice was quite rapid in what is now southern Alberta. Much of the rubble which had lain beneath the ice flow was swept along in the rush of the meltwaters. As these receded, only a shallow layer of top soil remained. For this reason, the relationship of the soil to the underlying bedrock is extremely important.

PROBLEM SOILS

The EID has its share of problem soils, caused by just such a relationship. These are known as "alkali" or "saline" soils. They occur where the underlying bedrock is made up of Cretaceous marine deposits that were laid down when the dinosaurs roamed. Applying irrigation water too heavily or without proper drainage can result in the water table rising to a point between 3 and 9 feet (1 and 3 metres) below the surface. The water acts as a vehicle for transporting the naturally occurring salts up from the bedrock and subsoil and toward the surface. Soil water is then removed through two processes: surface evaporation, and transpiration from the growing plants. This leaves the salt concentrated in the root zone and visible as a white "alkali" crust on the soil's surface. Lower soil productivity and significant decreases in crop yields result.

Investigations into just what types of agriculture could be viable in the Eastern Irrigation District date back to 1913 when the engineers and technicians of the Irrigation Surveys and Inspections Branch of the Department of the Interior began to classify land for irrigation purposes. Later, the CPR engaged its own specialists. One man who accepted a position as soil chemist and irrigation engineer with the CPR was Asael E. Palmer who, in 1917, had just completed a degree at Utah State Agricultural College. Having spent five years as a home-steader in the Turin area of south-central Alberta, Palmer was intimately ac-quainted with the properties of arid soils.

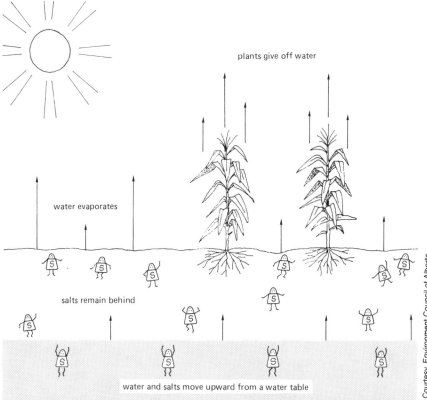

plants give off water

water evaporates

salts remain behind

water and salts move upward from a water table

Courtesy, Environment Council of Alberta.

Soil salinization occurs when mineral salts dissolved in water are deposited near soil surface, as water is drawn up into atmosphere. Heavy concentrations of salts result in condition known as "alkali."

In the summers of 1917 to 1920, he was assigned to conduct soil and irrigation studies on a block of land near Tilley. Part of his time was spent in the field, but he also worked in a well-equipped soil analysis laboratory established by the CPR in Calgary for use by their corps of soil scientists.

Here, in Dr. Palmer's own words, is his account of the soil classification controversy in the Tilley region:

> Dominion Government officials considered most of the land east of Brooks unsuitable [for irrigation], but the CPR officials were not willing to accept their verdict, for while the government soil specialists were capable men, their experience had been in more humid areas, and so their knowledge of arid soils was limited. Their reason for considering these soils unsuitable for irrigation was that there was a relatively high concentration of salt in the sub-soils. However, they overlooked the fact that most of the salt present was calcium sulphate (gypsum), which not only is low in its toxic effect on plants, but . . . has an ameliorating effect on the harmful properties of the other salts present. Actually, I seem to have been one of the first to discover this phenomenon, and I found it difficult to convince other soil chemists that there is such a relationship, although we had quite conclusive data to support my thesis. Now this ameliorating effect is generally recognized . . .
>
> As a result of our investigations I recommended that the area be irrigated, which recommendation was accepted by the CPR. The almost 50 years that have followed has seen these lands develop into a successful irrigation enterprise.
>
> (Oral History of A. E. Palmer, pp. 23-24)

This important work in soil classification is still continuing: the irrigation scientists and technologists of Alberta Agriculture work with the Eastern Irrigation District staff and water users. They bring more areas of suitable land under irrigation, as well as helping to manage those areas which are already "under the ditch" in the most effective and efficient manner.

Rough land along Red Deer, originally classified by CPR as irrigable.

FOUNDATIONS OF AGRICULTURE IN THE EID

BROOKS IRRIGATION EXPERIMENT STATION

Display at early
Brooks fair. Station
was located just
west of present-
day town.

Research into irrigation practices in Canada has been ongoing since the early years of this century. In addition to soil classification work, which took place before irrigation water was available, investigations into the best methods of applying water were also undertaken. Test, or experimental, stations were established by both the federal government and irrigation companies to determine the "duty of water" which is the mean depth of water required to produce maximum crop yields under varying soil conditions.

The Water Power and Reclamation Service, Department of the Interior, Government of Canada operated the Brooks Irrigation Experiment Station for more than ten years. The first sod was broken in June 1917, at a location just west of the present-day town, and seeding of crops was begun the following spring. From 1918 until the station was dismantled in 1927, the staff conducted experiments on the growing of alfalfa, peas, wheat, oats, barley, flax, potatoes, grass, beets, alfalfa seed and corn.

Federal government investigations into irrigation and its effects on cropping practices continued at other locations in southern Alberta. Lethbridge Research Station is perhaps the best known of these. It is still very actively involved in irrigation and other agricultural research.

DEMONSTRATION FARMS

The CPR established a demonstration farm at Brooks in 1916, where experimental work with both crops and livestock was carried out. Other demonstration farms were set up as early as 1914 at Tilley, Cassils and Lathom. The development of these areas of company-owned land arose from the need to expand

Agriculture train in Alberta, 1912.

upon the concept of "seed trains" or "agriculture trains" which had been operating for a number of years in Manitoba and Saskatchewan. These trains, containing exhibits designed to help settlers improve their farming methods, stopped at each station along the CPR lines for a brief three-hour period. This amount of time proved insufficient for farmers to grasp the principles of successful farming, with the result that few of them were able to apply the demonstrated techniques to their own farming operations. CPR officials believed a more permanent demonstration available to farmers on a full-time basis would be of greater benefit.

In 1912, Colonel J. S. Dennis, Jr. was in charge of the CPR's Department of Natural Resources, with headquarters in Calgary. It was at his instigation that a number of demonstration farms were established throughout western Canada, with the aim of showing settlers that mixed farming offered them a far better livelihood than straight grain farming. Far from trying to wow the locals with exotic crops or livestock, these company-owned and -staffed farms were operated to show what settlers could expect to accomplish in the first five to seven years of their occupancy — providing they had a small amount of investment capital and worked toward the objectives of stocking and operating their 160 acres as diversified farms.

Looking west across Demonstration Farm pea field toward Brooks, 1930's.

DON H. BARK

Although some trees and cuttings were planted at a site on the east edge of town in 1916, the demonstration farm at Brooks was not firmly established until 1918. Earlier, some extension work with contract holders in the Eastern Section had been initiated by the staff of the CPR's Irrigation Investigation Branch at Strathmore. Don Hurdman Bark had been Superintendent there since 1915, at which time the CPR enticed him away from a promising career in "duty of water" investigations in the western United States with an offer of $4,000 a year plus housing.

Mr. Bark seems to have been a very energetic man, who assembled a staff of able agriculturalists and irrigation men around him. They worked together to identify the difficulties associated with bringing land under irrigation, and then proposed solutions to these problems.

By the time World War I came to a close in 1918, three years of irrigation investigation had been completed in the Western Section by Bark and his associates. The development of the Brooks Demonstration Farm was stepped up after the armistice to prepare for the expected influx of settlers to the Eastern Section. In addition to its role as an efficient working model of a diversified farm, this project functioned as a test station, where experiments on diverse crops under irrigation were conducted.

Other experimental plots were located at Countess, Lathom, in the Imperial Colony and on the Bow Slope. In these locations, much of the irrigation and harvesting was contracted to farmers on whose land the plot was established.

ALFALFA HAY

Although the 1924 Annual Report of the Irrigation Investigation Branch reveals that a wide array of crops (including field peas, oats, barley, potatoes, sweet corn, field corn, white navy beans, mangel beets, and sugar beets) were under test, Mr. Bark is best remembered for his tireless (some might say, tiresome) promotion of alfalfa. This legume he regarded as "the king of forage crops." Not only could it be profitably produced for sale to livestock concerns outside the irrigation areas, but farmers could also develop a secondary source of income through feeding it to their own herds of cattle or sheep. By then returning the livestock manure to the fields, the farmers could further enhance the soil fertility, already promoted through the nitrogen-fixing capacity of the alfalfa.

ALFALFA SEED

Another aspect of alfalfa production dear to the heart of the irrepressible Bark was the growing of registered alfalfa seed. His efforts to promote this crop in the Western Section had been to no avail, but farmers in the Eastern Section proved more receptive. The early producers of alfalfa seed obtained excellent results. It was soon realized that the large population of wild bees, which inhabited the native grasslands, was a major contributor to this success. These tiny creatures were very

Government inspector sealing bags of registered Grimm alfalfa seed, 1924.

efficient at pollinating the crop, reportedly providing some lucky farmers with yields of up to 1,000 pounds per acre (1,120 kg/ha).

As production of this crop caught on, Bark was instrumental in organizing the Grimm Alfalfa Seed Growers' Association. This group was established in Brooks in 1923; and, by the following year, 100 area farmers had paid the $100 membership fee which entitled them to grow, clean and market registered Grimm alfalfa seed through the association. Their letterhead states that, since it is grown in the most northerly alfalfa seed-producing region in North America, seed produced in the Brooks area is "grown under such severe weather conditions that none but the very hardiest plants can survive and produce seed." This seed could then be counted upon to produce good crops under almost any climatic conditions on the continent.

One of the first signs of the group's presence in Brooks was the construction of their seed-cleaning plant and warehouse in 1923. It was billed as "the most up-to-date plant of its kind in the Dominion of Canada, if not the whole North American continent." The 34-foot (10.4 metre) tower, which housed the cleaning equipment, made the Grimm building the tallest in Brooks — with the exception of the grain elevators, of course. Another distinguishing feature was the electric light plant. This modern convenience permitted the operation of round-the-clock shifts. Now part of the Asgrow Seeds building complex, the original warehouse is still standing.

OTHER ACTIVITIES

The Brooks Demonstration Farm operated under Bark's dynamic (and sometimes, flamboyant) leadership until the Eastern Irrigation District was formed in May of 1935. Although he was killed in an auto accident later that year, Bark initiated many programs of lasting agricultural importance to this area. Some of these include:

(1) growing and marketing pure grain and grass seed;

(2) furthering the cause of livestock improvement by importing and disseminating good breeding stock to settlers;

(3) reinforcing the principles on which the demonstration farm operated through publication of a newsletter, *Irrigation Bulletin*, distributed free of charge to all water users in the Eastern Section;

(4) supporting and promoting the exhibition of crops at local, provincial, national and international expositions. This resulted in the Brooks area becoming widely known across North America for the high quality of its forage crops, seed grains and vegetables;

(5) helping to organize and promote community and school fairs to exhibit local produce. In 1921, five such events were held in the Eastern Section, all deemed very successful: the Mat-zi-win Agricultural Society Third Annual Fair, Third Annual Seed Fair, and School Fair in Brooks; a School Fair in Bassano, and a First Annual Patricia Fair;

(6) publicizing, and otherwise encouraging, the development of local non-profit agricultural co-operatives, such as Brooks Alfalfa Feeders Limited, which furnished cattle to local farmers for a short-term feeding period;

(7) operating a labour bureau, in order to help farmers obtain seasonal labourers;

Irrigation Investigation Branch display, CPR Fair, Bassano, 1919.

Just in time for Christmas dinner.

(8) providing assistance in marketing crops and livestock. For instance, staff at the Irrigation Investigation Branch helped to organize the killing, plucking, grading and packing of turkeys every fall for a number of years in the early 1920's. In the fall of 1923, for instance, over 8,000 turkeys, weighing in at 81,115 pounds (36,790 kg) were processed at "community turkey kills" held at Duchess, Patricia, Brooks, Cassils, Rainier, Jenny Lind, Bassano and Gem.

(9) producing, and selling to local settlers at a very nominal price, trees, shrubs, small fruits and vines. Individual families, as well as community groups, were encouraged to obtain, set out and care for these plants. In any one year up to 16,000 seedlings were distributed. These were much prized for their ability to turn the farm building site into a calm and green oasis on the wind swept prairie. Demonstration farm employees were also instrumental in planning and maintaining railway parks at Brooks and Bassano, as well as two town parks in Brooks.

Crates of turkeys delivered from the Bow Slope to Brooks for shipment by rail.

GUS GRIFFIN

In 1918, Augustus "Gus" Griffin was appointed superintendent of operation and maintenance for the CPR's Eastern Section. Born and raised in an irrigated area of California, Griffin was widely known for his outstanding abilities as an irrigation engineer. He was much in demand as a consultant on the design, operation and construction problems encountered by irrigation and power companies.

A slight, bespectacled man, Griffin was so unassuming that he was often mistaken for one of the labourers on the project. Nevertheless, he had the reputation of being a "doer" — not only did he work very hard himself, but he had the skills to inspire others to great accomplishments. These qualities, no doubt, contributed to his success with the CPR. After ably executing his duties in the Eastern Section for 14 years, he made steady progress up the career ladder until, in 1942, he was appointed manager of the CPR's Department of Natural Resources in Calgary.

Despite his tremendous successes in life, those who knew him say he was very personable, and able to chat comfortably with everyone. Some of Griffin's correspondence files are still in existence. They reveal the lengths to which he went to help the many individuals who solicited his advice.

One young woman from Bassano wrote to the Brooks CPR offices in March of 1925, requesting some tomato seeds, as well as information on how best to ensure their healthy growth. Soon, she received her seeds, together with instructions for maintaining the tender seedlings in a hotbed. The letter, dispatched by one of Griffin's associates, stopped short of advising how best to transplant the seedlings. Nine days later, another letter to the same woman was mailed. It seems to be an afterthought to the earlier one and was dictated, this time, by Griffin himself. He provides lovingly detailed instructions about how, if one was without benefit of a hotbed, it would be equally effective to start the seeds in small boxes or cans, keeping them in a sunny window of the house. How best to acclimatise the tender shoots to the outdoors, before transplanting them to the garden, is also described.

When one considers the tremendous responsibilities Griffin had in overseeing the operation and maintenance of the entire irrigation network, his willingness to respond, personally and thoroughly, to such a modest request is quite remarkable. There are many examples of this concern for others in Griffin's papers, as individuals and groups from all over the Eastern Section, the Province of Alberta, the Dominion of Canada, and many of the states in the Union wrote to him for information and advice. It may seem unusual to contact a well-known irrigation engineer about trees and gardens, but Gus Griffin was equally renowned for his expertise in the field of horticulture. In fact, he corresponded with nurseries all over North America, and exchanged seeds and cuttings with such notables as Luther Burbank of California.

Much of the plant material for which Brooks has become famous was collected by Griffin from natural settings in Alberta; many specimens were obtained from areas within what is now the EID. His diary reveals that on his customary rambles about the countryside, he collected large numbers of native plants, shrubs and trees. Most of these, he brought back to Brooks for propagation. In 1918, he collected chokecherries, bullberries and saskatoons along the Red Deer River at Emerson Bridge, and gooseberries, strawberries and violets at Steveville. The river flats at Gregory Ferry provided him with cottonwood seedlings for transplant to the area around the CPR staff residences. Steveville seems to have been one of his favourite spots, as he later obtained willows, dogwood, wild raspberries and a "sundry lot of trees and plants" from that same area.

Griffin continued to collect native plant specimens throughout his years in Brooks, crossbreeding many of them with other varieties in order to enhance their hardiness, beauty and productivity. Today, gardeners throughout North America are familiar with the Brooks sandcherry; Waterton mock orange; Jumping Pound cherry; Strathmore crabapple; Griffin, Brooks 4 and Brooks 6 poplars; and Altaglow, a white saskatoon. All are products of Griffin's pioneering efforts in collecting and improving native plants.

Griffin, and later the staff of the Provincial Horticultural Station, were instrumental in putting the name of Brooks and area on the horticultural map. As well, many local residents, through their work with vegetables, flowers and trees, have contributed to the common fund of horticultural knowledge.

Part of the original orchard planted by Griffin, Brooks headquarters.

HEADQUARTERS FARM

In addition to their water management duties, the staff was expected to plant and harvest crops on CPR "reservations." This term was used to designate land withheld from sale and set aside for the company's own buildings and operations. Every spring, ditchriders, among others, were issued seed to be planted on their reservations. Yields from these small, farmed holdings were carefully recorded and included in the superintendent's annual report. That of 1920, for instance, states that over 740 acres (300 ha) were farmed by the CPR in what is now the EID. Most of the lands were planted to hay and grain, which were used to feed the company's huge stable of work horses.

The Headquarters Farm, located to the northwest of the office building and residences in Brooks, was by far the largest of these corporate farms. The stately elegance and restful shade of Evergreen Park is a living reminder of the days when the Headquarters Farm covered most of what is now the western half of the Town of Brooks. An entry in Gus Griffin's personal diary records that, on April 11, 1918, an area south of the office, formerly used as a tennis court, was broken with a walking plow. Thus began the operation of the Headquarters, or West, Farm. Later that season, larger areas were broken, including more than 100 acres (40 ha) north of the railway, some of which had previously been used for the Brooks town dump. By the end of 1920, the Headquarters Farm comprised over 400 acres (160 ha), and the value of its product that year was almost $15,000.

Under the able direction of a head gardener and an army of labourers (who were sometimes seconded from other projects), the Headquarters Farm functioned as a nursery. Thousands of tree cuttings were grown there to be given to many settlements on the project and to local CPR employees. In later years, trees from Brooks travelled farther afield, to beautify CPR station grounds throughout the province. Much prized by the dining car chefs on the CPR passenger trains were the flavoursome fruits and crisp vegetables seasonally available at Brooks. An inventory of the seed and crops produced in the years 1921 through 1925 reveals the diversity in production: seven varieties of beans, four varieties of peas, onion seed, and three types of sunflower seed, along with large quantities of seed grain and forage crops. The quality of these products was top-notch — they consistently won honours at such prestigious exhibitions as Toronto's Royal Winter Fair.

Perhaps the most enduring reminders of the Brooks Headquarters Farm are the shade trees, windbreaks and fruit trees that may be seen on many farmsteads and on the streets of most communities around the District. The towering white spruce that line the driveway from First Avenue up to the EID headquarters were planted in 1919, the same year that the CPR provided 400 poplars, free-of-charge, to the residents of Brooks for planting along other streets.

Every spring during the late 1920's, Griffin sent out a circular letter urging canal superintendents, water masters and ditchriders to place their orders for "windbreaks, avenue, roadside and individual specimens, and fruits and orna-mentals." Employees were exhorted not to order more than they could promptly plant or care for during the season. Detailed instructions for the cultivation of each of the various species were provided. Some plants, such as chokecherries and golden glow were in plentiful supply, and could be ordered in quantity by everyone. Other varieties, such as spruce, oak, weeping willow and grape vines, were in short supply. Griffin allowed these precious seedlings to go home only with employees who promised to take "extra good care" of them!

The 1925 Annual Report states that the number of trees sent out to field reservations from the Brooks Headquarters Farm (8,454) was almost as great as the number sold to settlers by the Irrigation Investigation Branch through their Demonstration Farm (10,964). Since many of the CPR's original reservations have been sold to private owners over the years, farm homes throughout the area are graced with lovely old trees that owe their start to Gus Griffin's tender ministrations.

Today, the results of these early efforts at beautification are appreciated by all who travel through the District. However, Griffin's superiors at the CPR Department of Natural Resources in Calgary were not always so impressed with his dedication. A. S. Dawson, Griffin's supervisor, sent the following memo to him:

CANADIAN PACIFIC RAILWAY COMPANY

INTER-DEPARTMENT
CORRESPONDENCE   FILE   C.E.418

Calgary, Alberta. February 4th, 1926.

Mr. Griffin:

he - your Requisition N.R.5073-B.

As the Manager has on more than one occasion criticised the scale on which horticultural work
has been carried on by you at Brooks Headquarters, I
am afraid I could not obtain his approval of this order.

Is it all stuff that has not yet been
tried out at Brooks, or is it in part or as a whole,
supplemental to varieties already planted?

A.S. Dawson,
Chief Engineer.

ASD/MN

2-yr-old cottonwood and willow saplings
grown from seed, 1919.

Back went Griffin's reply, diplomatically stating that he had not previously been able to obtain Chinese Elm and that, although butternut, cedar and arbor vitae had already been planted at Brooks, more were needed to replace those that had died. We can only assume that Mr. Naismith, then manager of the DNR, eventually gave his approval for this order. Specimens of these varieties were growing at the Headquarters Farm and at other locations in the District when a complete inventory of the CPR's horticultural holdings was compiled ten years later.

ALBERTA HORTICULTURAL RESEARCH CENTRE (HORT STATION)

When it became obvious that the CPR would be disposing of its interest in the Eastern Section, Griffin wanted to ensure the continuation of his beloved horticultural work. Accordingly, the company made overtures to the University of Alberta and to the Departments of Agriculture of both the provincial and federal governments about taking over the Headquarters and Demonstration Farms. By 1935, the Alberta Department of Agriculture had declared its interest in the project, and a long-term lease for the Provincial Horticultural Station was a condition of the CPR-EID transfer agreement.

The former Demonstration Farm, located on what was then the eastern edge of Brooks, continued to propagate small trees and shrubs for shelterbelts, and was also involved in some experimental work with livestock. At what had been the Headquarters Farm, located on the western edge of town, the initial task was to record all the plant materials already established there. This work occupied three men for over a year. A plant breeding program, aimed at producing better varieties of fruits hardy in the climatic extremes of the prairies, was also begun.

Work at the hort station continued, unabated, until the mid-1940's. At that time, the Eastern Irrigation District board came under pressure to sell some of the former CPR farmlands. The population of Brooks had begun to increase and, in

J. L. Carroll Photographics Ltd.

BEFORE: New site of Hort. Station along main highway, Spring 1950.

Brooks Bulletin.

AFTER: Alberta Horticultural Research Centre. Annual Field Day, August 1977.

1945, more than 25 acres (10 ha) were sold from the east section of the horticultural station. Further land was lost in 1946, this time from the west side, to provide for the expansion of another government operation, the Pheasant Hatchery. By 1950, urban growth had increased to the extent that demand for land forced the EID to request the removal of the hort station to a new location.

The site that the station had occupied for 15 years was exchanged for almost 250 acres (100 ha) of irrigable land located just southeast of the townsite. Known as the "Lendrum Farm," this parcel was much larger in area than the original site, but its soil was not of such good quality. To improve irrigability and drainage, much land reclamation was undertaken during the nine-year moving period. Such a span of time was necessary to transfer all the plant materials and erect the required buildings. It must have been difficult for the staff to leave their work-place, which was famous throughout western Canada, for a stretch of bare prairie grass. They found themselves right back at "square one" — just where Gus Griffin had been so many years before when he began breaking the sod and planting the first saplings on the Brooks Headquarters Farm.

With the application of water from the EID system, and the hard work of the staff, the new station began to take shape. By 1959, when the move had been completed, the formerly cheerless site had begun to take on a lush green ap-pearance. Today the Alberta Horticultural Research Centre, like its predecessor, the Provincial Horticultural Station, is famous for its lovely grounds. The high quality of its experimental work, and its horticulture and shelterbelt programs are renowned province-wide. The staff of 45 permanent and 65 seasonal workers is primarily involved in applied research programs to meet the needs of the develop-ing commercial horticultural industries of the province.

Verdant shelterbelts, herds of sleek cattle, solid stands of grain and fields of blooming alfalfa — all are signs of the principles of successful irrigation farming in action. Today's farmers have put into practice the agricultural tenets that the CPR promoted through its demonstration farms, and which Bark and Griffin advanced. They would surely be pleased if they could see the EID's tremendous progress over the past sixty-odd years, built upon the twin foundations of an efficient irrigation system and the practice of diversified farming.

CURRENT AGRICULTURAL PRACTICES IN THE EID

CULTURAL METHODS SPECIFIC TO IRRIGATION

Sound technical knowledge is a prerequisite to success in irrigation farm-ing. By comparison with dryland operations, irrigation necessitates larger capital and operating investments; so, to be cost-effective, it must result in higher per-acre yields. Generally, in the EID, the returns in production are commensurate with the expenses incurred.

The following are some of the factors that account for the added costs of irrigation farming:

1) When sufficient water is provided, and the yield potential thereby in-creased, crops also need more nutrients. Thus, it is important to apply the correct type of fertilizer in sufficient amounts so that lack of nutrients does not inhibit growth. If this is not done, higher yields can deplete the soils very rapidly, resulting in situations where both the macronutrients (nitro-gen, phosphorus, potash and sulphur) and micronutrients (such as zinc and copper) need replenishment. If such situations are allowed to occur, additional expenditures are necessary to correct them.

2) When irrigation water is applied by the surface or flood method, good water management must be practiced so as to ensure that soil nutrients are not washed away with the groundwater. In cases where nutrients are lost, more fertilizer will be needed.

3) Extra deep tillage, ripping and plowing are sometimes necessary in order to ensure water penetration, particularly with the solonetzic soils which occur in the District. Tillage is also undertaken in order to return to the soil the large amounts of straw and other organic matter which result from higher yields. Plowing is a technique which is especially useful in conjunction with the application of topical herbicides; if the organic matter is not worked deeply back into the soil, then the chemical will often work on the surface debris, rather than on the weeds for which it was originally intended.

4) In addition to the cost of grading or levelling land, which is usually hired out to earth-moving contractors, most irrigation farmers find it necessary to "float" their land one or more times a year. A float is a tractor-drawn implement with a blade mounted about halfway down its considerable length. It is used to level off small high spots and fill in the depressions which result from cultivation. Even minor irregularities in the surface of a field can prevent an even application of water, and interfere with maximum yields.

In the years since irrigation first began in the District, specialized agricultural practices have evolved to minimize the accompanying problems and to ensure the continuing economic health of this sector of Alberta's agricultural industry.

HOW WE IRRIGATE

When a farmer wants to irrigate his land, he must contact the local water district supervisor (ditchrider) to "order" the amount of water he needs. Water district supervisors live on small parcels of land owned by the District. These were set aside by the CPR when the system was first built, to provide each ditchrider with a residence near his worksites.

Not long after the Eastern Section was established, an elder from the Blackfoot reserve, traveling in company with Charles Galbraith, a CPR employee, christened the ditchrider reservations with Blackfoot names. A few of these names are still in use today, despite the fact that many of the company's reservations were closed out in 1922 when the advent of mechanization resulted in the enlargement of the individual districts.

"Cowoki" is the Blackfoot word for "corner." Although there has not been a ditchrider reservation there for many years, the name is still used to identify an irrigation reservoir located north of Tilley. Pitau, meaning "eagle," is located northeast of Bassano.

Some of the present-day water district supervisors live on original reservation sites, but the names were changed from the Blackfoot to those of CPR employees killed overseas in World War I. The Cockerill district, for instance, was originally named "Nartosarpi," Blackfoot for "old sun."

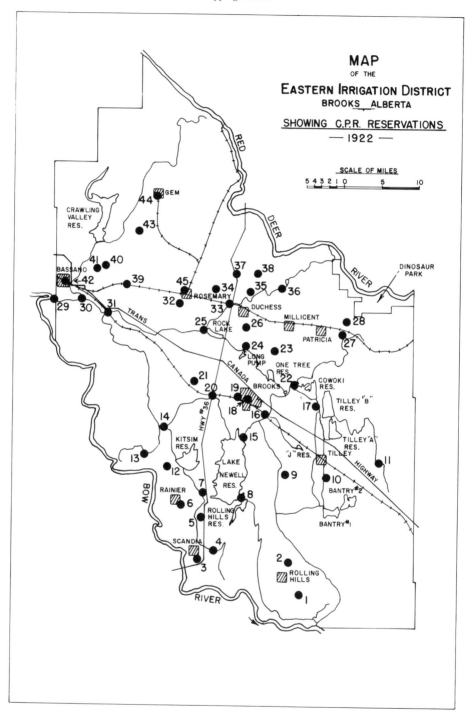

MAP
OF THE
EASTERN IRRIGATION DISTRICT
BROOKS__ALBERTA

SHOWING C.P.R. RESERVATIONS
— 1922 —

The name by which the reservation was originally designated appears first. In brackets, Blackfoot names are given correct spellings and meanings where known, courtesy Blackfoot Studies Dept., Old Sun Community College, Blackfoot Reserve. The most recent name of reservation is given last.

#	NAME(S)	ORIGINAL LAND LOCATION
1.	No. 11	SW 28-14-13
2.	No. 13	SW 17-15-13
3.	Sauki (Sokii — "prairie")	NW 17-15-15
4.	Otopustan (unknown) Ross	NW 22-15-15
5.	Greentree	NW 8-16-15
6.	Minipoka (Mina-poka — "berry child") Bow Slope Watermaster	NE 23-16-16
7.	Bow Slope Spillway	SE 32-16-15
8.	Rolling Hills Headgates	NE 30-16-14
9.	Elizabeth	NE 7-17-13
10.	Pokappini (Poka-pini — "small eyes") Gilbertson	SE 7-17-12
11.	No. 2	SW 20-17-11
12.	Kitsim (Kitsim — "gate" or "door")	NE 16-17-16
13.	Ow'arkos (Awaksi — "antelope")	SE 25-17-17
14.	Antelope Creek Siphon (Ass't Water Master)	NW 9-18-16
15.	Bantry Headgates	SW 5-18-14
16.	Brooks Aqueduct	Pt SW 23 and Pt SE 22-18-14
17.	Mutsinau (Matsi-nawa — "no man") Kinnear	NE 26-18-13
18.	Brooks Headquarters	32-18-14
19.	Brooks Ditchrider	NW 31-18-14
20.	Cassils Siphon	NW 34-18-15
21.	Matoka (Mataki — "potato")	NE 7-19-15
22.	Cowoki (Koki — "corner")	SE 9-19-13
23.	Sitsikau (Siksika — "blackfoot")	SE 36-19-14
24.	Long, later Baker	SE 5-20-14
25.	Nartosarpi (Nato-sapi — "old sun") Cockerill	SW 16-20-15
26.	Minnarpis (unknown) Wilkins	NE 17-20-14
27.	Princess, later Sand Creek	NE 9-20-12
28.	Nimexi (unknown)	NW 22-20-12
29.	Bassano Dam	1-21-19
30.	Little Dam	S½ 3-21-18
31.	Lathom	SE 30-20-17
32.	Manning Butte	NE 35-20-16
33.	Istoikum (Istokimi — "cold water") McKenzie	N½ 36-20-15
34.	Kokay (Koki — "corner")	NE 10-21-15
35.	Welch	SE 9-21-14
36.	Sam Howe, later Haffner	NE 7-21-13
37.	Spotsiki (Spotsikoyi — "sand hills")	NW 19-21-14
38.	Imperial	NW 22-21-13
39.	Countess Watermaster & Ditchrider	SE 15-21-17
40.	Owotan (Awootan — "shield")	NE 30-21-17
41.	McLean	SE 25-21-18
42.	Bassano Headquarters	NE 17-21-18
43.	Pitau (Pita — "eagle")	SW 24-22-17
44.	Gem Watermaster & Ditchrider	NW 9-23-16
45.	Rosemary	NE 1-21-16

DUTIES OF WATER DISTRICT SUPERVISORS

The water district supervisors of today, like the ditchriders of the past, are the District employees who work most directly with water users. They are responsible for keeping all the supply canals and ditches, control structures and drainage ditches in efficient operating condition, seven days a week throughout

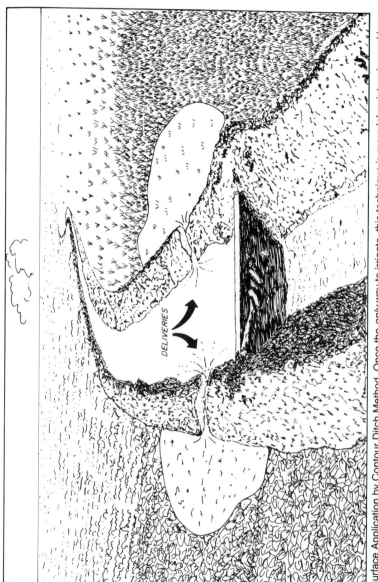

Surface Application by Contour Ditch Method. Once the *only* way to irrigate, this technique is more labor-intensive and less efficient than many newer ones. It is still used on rough, or unlevelled, lands.

the irrigation season. The system has been designed so that the supply ditches convey water to the highest elevation on most farms. Control structures, known as turnouts or headgates, are installed at this point to regulate the flow of water into a network of ditches in the farm field. On some farms, the water first enters a reservoir from which it is pumped to sprinkler systems.

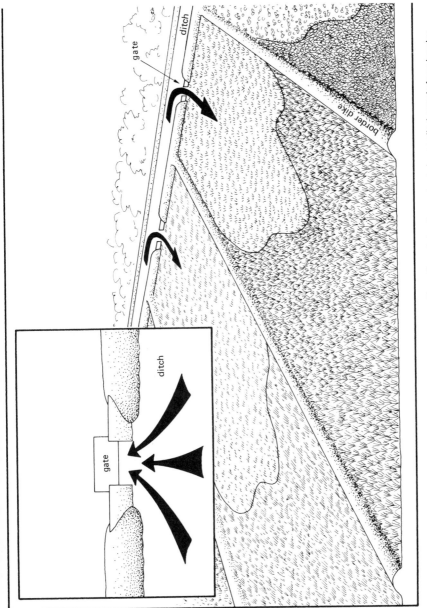

Surface Application by Border Dyke Method. Mechanized land levelling allows irrigation water to be applied evenly from border ditches, or between border dykes, as shown above. About 60 per cent of the EID's irrigated lands are watered by some method of surface application.

Environment Council of Alberta, 1982.

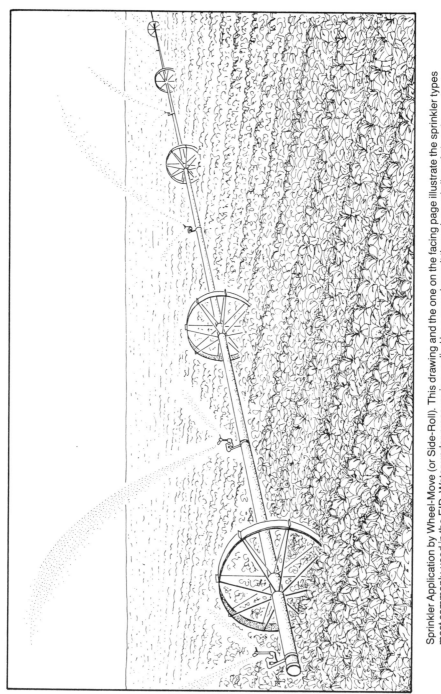

Sprinkler Application by Wheel-Move (or Side-Roll). This drawing and the one on the facing page illustrate the sprinkler types most commonly-used in the EID. Water under pressure is supplied by a pumping unit through a main line of pipe. An engine in the centre of the lateral rolls the unit between positions (or sets).

Environment Council of Alberta, 1982.

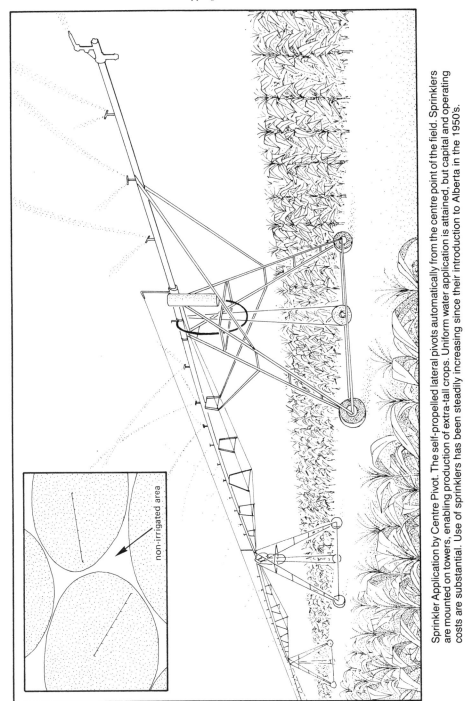

non-irrigated area

Sprinkler Application by Centre Pivot. The self-propelled lateral pivots automatically from the centre point of the field. Sprinklers are mounted on towers, enabling production of extra-tall crops. Uniform water application is attained, but capital and operating costs are substantial. Use of sprinklers has been steadily increasing since their introduction to Alberta in the 1950's.

Environment Council of Alberta, 1982.

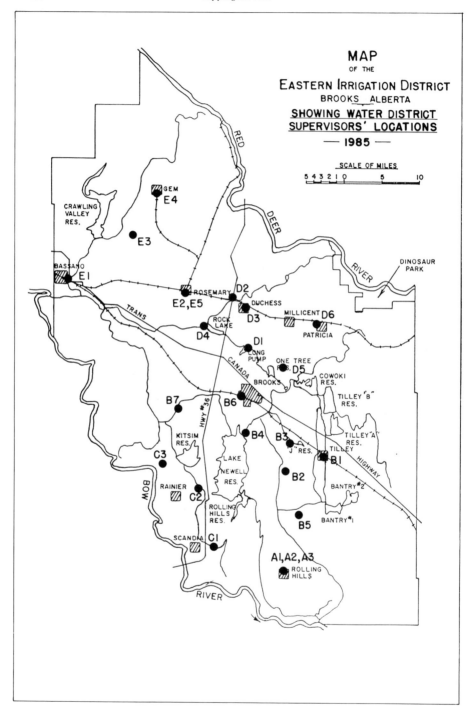

MAP
OF THE
EASTERN IRRIGATION DISTRICT
BROOKS ALBERTA
SHOWING WATER DISTRICT
SUPERVISORS' LOCATIONS
— 1985 —

SCALE OF MILES
5 4 3 2 1 0 5 10

CROPPING PRACTICES

1983 EID CROP CENSUS*

Crop	Hectares Planted	Acres Planted
*Wheat	30,825	76,168
*Alfalfa Hay	26,745	66,086
*Barley	10,446	25,812
*Tame Pasture	8,437	20,848
*Alfalfa Seed	4,475	11,058
*Silage	3,017	7,455
*Green Feed	2,218	5,482
*Oats	1,892	4,677
Canola	1,773	4,382
Summerfallow	1,629	4,020
New Development	1,399	3,457
Flax	1,232	3,046
Potatoes	1,092	2,700
*Grass Hay	975	2,409
Mustard	632	1,562
Seed Peas	471	1,164
Corn	456	1,125
*Mixed Grain	373	920
Other vegetables (carrots, cabbage, beans, pumpkin, squash, etc.)	367	906
Yards and Shrubs	267	660
Sugar Beets	150	371
Rye	59	145
Russian Wild Rye	49	120
Fenugreek	37	92
Timothy Seed	8	20
Lawn Turf	8	20
TOTAL IRRIGATED LAND IN CROP	99,032	244,711
TOTAL LIVESTOCK-RELATED CROPS (INCLUDING WHEAT)	89,404	220,915
TOTAL LIVESTOCK-RELATED CROPS (EXCLUDING WHEAT)	58,579	144,747

*adapted from *Eastern Irrigation District, Forty-Ninth Annual Report, 1983*, p. 17.

A glance at the table above reveals that wheat is the largest single crop raised in the Eastern Irrigation District. Because the figures do not make distinctions between the different varieties of each crop (i.e., feed barley vs. malting barley, or sweet corn vs. field corn), it is assumed that most, if not all, of those crops marked with an asterisk were grown for livestock feed. Given this assumption, the table clearly shows that, of the over 244,711 acres (99,000 ha) cropped in 1983, almost 60 per cent was devoted to the growing of feed. This percentage is probably rather conservative, as it is likely that some portions of a number of other crops were also used for feed. The crop census clearly reveals that the EID and its environs depend heavily on a livestock economy.

LIVESTOCK

The production of beef cattle is of primary importance in the District; in 1983, there were 25,000 cow-calf units pastured on EID-owned grassland, and an equal number on private grassland, making beef cattle the single most important livestock industry. Several commercial feedlots operate within the District, and, together with numerous farm-based operations, they finish 50,000 head of feeder cattle annually. Beef cattle producers make up a very large majority of the 500 local livestock producers, while there are only a few operations producing other kinds of animals on a commercial scale. Among the non-beef producers are 50 hog operations, 15 sheep farmers, 36 dairy farms and 9 poultry producers.

Estimated Numbers of Livestock in the EID*

Poultry	125,000
Beef Cattle (cows)	50,000
Sheep (ewes)	2,000
Dairy Cattle (cows)	2,400
Hogs (sows)	2,000
Major feedlot capacity (beef cattle)	50,000

*Source: Local Statistics (1984), Alberta Agriculture, Brooks District Office

In addition to producing forage crops (primarily alfalfa) and feed grains for the animals raised in the District, the Eastern Irrigation District functions as a "security area" for the surrounding dryland farmers and ranchers. In years when drought and other calamities stunt their hay and grain crops, these people can almost always make up the shortfall through purchases from the neighboring irrigated area.

ALFALFA HAY

Over the years, more and more land in the District has been turned over to alfalfa hay. The advent of better transportation networks in recent times has made it possible to market our produce across the country, the continent, and even overseas. EID-grown alfalfa hay is trucked by local firms to markets in other parts of the province, as well as to British Columbia, Saskatchewan, and parts of the United States.

With the development of the dehydration process, it has become possible to ship alfalfa over much greater distances at a nominal cost. Japan is a principal export market, while other Asian countries are potential buyers of the product. Here's how the dehydration process works: alfalfa is chopped up finely and fed into the dehydrator where moisture is removed. In the next stage, a controlled amount of water is injected back into the forage before it is shaped into small cubes. In this cubed form, the alfalfa can be handled more easily and shipped more cheaply than in the bulkier baled form. At present, two locally-owned and - operated processing plants are profitably engaged in this venture.

Swather at work in a field of blooming alfalfa hay.

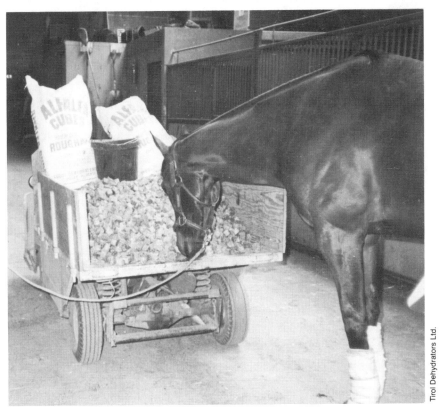

Alfalfa cubes are an important EID export.

ALFALFA SEED AND LEAFCUTTER BEES

Alfalfa seed is the fifth most important crop, in terms of the area of land on which it is grown, in the EID. Since it was first introduced to this area, it has provided many local farmers with an opportunity for diversification. In the last twenty years, however, a growing number of water users have begun to specialize in raising alfalfa seed. This, in turn, has resulted in another form of specialization: the culture of leafcutter bees.

Soon after alfalfa seed crops were first grown in this area, it was discovered that yields could be dramatically increased if the crops were pollinated by native wild bees. As the amount of cultivated land increased, however, the natural habitat of these bees was destroyed. This, in turn, resulted in a decline in seed yields.

In an effort to regain higher yields, domesticated honey bees were used to pollinate alfalfa. Research and experience quickly demonstrated that their effectiveness was limited. Young worker bees soon learned to avoid the unpleasant "slap" which accompanied a full frontal assault on the alfalfa blossom. Instead, they learned to reach in from the side to extract the nectar. This new tactic suited the bees and their keepers very well, but was of little benefit to the alfalfa seed growers. "Tripping" of the blossom was the very process needed to trigger seed formation by the alfalfa plant.

Leafcutter bee shelters in an alfalfa seed field.

Ongoing experimentation aimed at increased alfalfa seed yields, carried out at the Lethbridge Research Station, revealed that a species of small bee, known as the leafcutter, was a very efficient alfalfa pollinator.

In the early 1960's one or two local farmers began importing leafcutter bees from the U.S. for that specific purpose. Since that time, the number of operators in the EID has steadily increased: they now number approximately fifty. Known as pollinators, most of these individuals culture the bees for use in their own alfalfa seed fields, but some also provide a custom pollinating service.

In addition to their season's work in pollinating alfalfa blossoms, female leafcutters lay a string of egg cells inside the "tunnels" in their hives. The first generation of bees dies at the end of its season, but the larvae are carefully overwintered and then incubated under controlled conditions so they are ready to be set out again when the next pollinating season begins.

The bee shelters are large wooden boxes, painted in bright colors or bold black and white geometric patterns and set out in the alfalfa fields. Inside, there are more patterns. Both interior and exteriors designs help to orient the bees and are especially useful when the colonies are first set outside. The motif on the outside helps the bee locate her "housing complex" while the one on the inside aids in finding her own "apartment."

The ability to successfully incubate new colonies in this district has resulted in production being more than sufficient for local demand. Most of this surplus is now marketed in the parts of the United States from which the EID pollinators originally purchased their stocks.

HONEY

Honey bee apiculture is also well-established in the EID. In 1984, there were about 10 commercial apiarists managing approximately 12,000 colonies or hives. Travellers about the District will be familiar with the sight of groups of hives, each made up of a stack of small rectangular boxes, called "supers," located in the corners of fields or in the leafy shelter of trees around abandoned farmsteads.

In terms of total production, the EID is the second most important honey-producing area in the province. Although the Peace River district, in its best years, produces more honey per hive than does the EID, production levels in the north are not consistent. The presence of irrigation water in our District means that, even in very dry years, there will always be some honey crop. And in years when other conditions are favourable, the EID's honey yields can be as high as 198 lb. (90 kg) per hive, with an average of 154 lb. (70 kg).

Brooks Bulletin.

Bee yard in late fall. Inverted pails contain sugar syrup which bees will store for over-winter food supply.

This crop stability is a marketing advantage for the EID's honey producers. Most of our honey comes from alfalfa blooms. Many important markets, especially those in Western Europe, are primarily interested in alfalfa and clover honey.

Many of our early settlers kept one or two hives for their own use, but commercial-size apiaries were first recorded in Brooks in the late 1920's. One of these early apiarists was a Mrs. O. Henry, who is said to have kept 200 colonies of bees. Described as a good business manager and a capable beekeeper, she was a featured speaker at the Alberta Beekeepers' Association Convention in 1935. Her talk was entitled "Can a Woman Run an Apiary?" One can only assume that her answer to that question was a resounding "yes!"

Over the years, more EID residents became involved in commercial apiculture, with the result that a plant for processing pasteurized honey was established at Bassano in 1954. Both creamed and liquid honey were produced at this facility until 1982, when the operation was bought out by another firm, and the plant closed.

Despite the closure, local honey production continues on a large scale. The EID's long growing season and the availability of irrigation water are of great assistance to the hard-working honey bee as she gathers rich pollen and nectar from the alfalfa fields, and manufactures the sweet ambrosia that has made our District so well known in the honey-consuming world.

VEGETABLES

Although vegetable production has not been as important in the EID as in more southerly regions of the province, in 1983 there were almost 6,000 acres

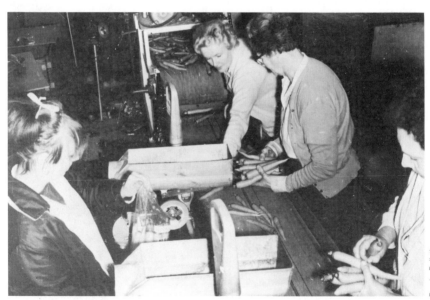

Carrot packaging, Newell Vegetable Co-op, 1968.

Brooks Bulletin.

(2,400 ha) planted to a variety of vegetable crops. Of these, potatoes accounted for almost half of the total area. Both chipping and table potatoes are produced here, and storage and packing facilities are available locally. At one time, potato chips were also manufactured at two plants in Brooks, but one facility burned, and the other closed down.

Carrots are washed and packaged, or diced and frozen, at a processing plant in Brooks. Originally set up as a growers' co-operative in the 1960's, the operation is now privately owned and serves as a marketing agency for other vegetables grown in the EID: corn, rutabaga, cabbage, beans, parsnips, pumpkin and squash.

Unique to the EID is the heating of a large, commercial greenhouse by the exhaust from a natural gas compressor station. An alternate heat source, for times when the compressor is not operating, is provided by boilers. Water from the irrigation system, with the addition of water-soluble nutrients, feeds the crops. Tomatoes have proved to be the No. 1 best-seller. Some are sold locally, but most of the crop is shipped to wholesalers in Calgary and Toronto.

Production of peas and beans was first introduced to the District in the 1920's. Although the acreage is not as great as it once was, a few farmers continue to produce, under contract, these and other specialty crops. The latter, grown occasionally or on a small scale, include: canary seed, radish seed, triticale, fenugreek, fababeans, dry beans, lentils and grain corn.

As the trend toward crop diversification continues, and the necessary market and processing facilities become available, a great number of farmers will likely become involved in the production of these and other alternative cash crops.

SOD FARMS AND NURSERY CROPS

Traditionally, the vegetable garden has been the farm woman's realm. Producing the food to nourish her family through the long winter has always been a source of pride. Friendly competition is a sport among avid gardeners. To be first to enjoy the season's vine-ripened tomatoes or to produce the largest jack-o-lantern for Hallowe'en adds zest to the toil of tilling, planting and harvesting.

Some of the busiest places in Brooks in the spring planting season are those where bedding plants are sold. At present, two greenhouse operators cater to this trade.

Flowering plants, as well as vegetables, are in popular demand, for while the vegetable garden answers a practical need, it is the front yard that delights the eye, with its colourful blooms and cool spread of green lawn. So important is grass underfoot to the homeowners of the area that two sod farms operate in the EID. These same two growers also have tree nurseries.

After the last vegetables and fruits have been canned or frozen and the leaves have dropped from the trees and the smell of winter is on the air, it seems the need for growing things remains. Greenhouse operators come to the rescue, again, with an array of house plants — easy-to-grow varieties for those with a brown thumb, along with more exotic, demanding species to challenge the expert.

RIPPLE EFFECTS FROM IRRIGATION

ECONOMIC EFFECTS

TRANSPORTATION

From the early days of irrigation, agricultural marketing and processing operations have been built upon the high yields and good quality of our local crops. At first, the CPR lines provided the only realistic form of transportation for both produce and passengers. In later years, a broad network of municipal and provincial roadways was gradually constructed, with the result that almost all District communities are now linked by either primary or secondary highways. The Trans-Canada Highway slashes its way across our local area in a diagonal line from Bassano to Tilley, and is our principal access route to markets. Most farmers are within a very short distance of the grid of gravelled roads built and maintained by the County of Newell No. 4. Along these arteries, farmers move their produce to local processing or storage facilities, or to loading facilities for transport to more distant markets. The main railway lines still ship goods in and out of the area, while highway transport services are provided by the more than twenty local trucking firms.

Crop duster at work.

Brooks Bulletin

Municipal airports are located at both Bassano and Brooks, and primarily serve small passenger aircraft. Air freight is not a factor at present, save for the cargoes of insecticides and herbicides carried by those aerial acrobats — the crop sprayers. In the cool of early summer mornings and late evenings, the roar of their dive bombings is audible for miles in the stillness. Skimming low across the field, the plane looses a fine chemical mist that drifts out and gradually settles down over the crop. At the fenceline, the spraying ceases as the aircraft swoops upward. After a wide banking turn, the plane settles down over the fields again, leaving another gentle plume of spray in its wake. Crop "dusting" is practiced throughout the Eastern Irrigation District as a speedy, cost-effective and comprehensive method of crop protection.

AGRICULTURAL PROCESSING

In addition to the vegetable processing and alfalfa dehydration plants discussed above, other agricultural processors, most of which are related to the livestock industry, are located in the EID. Brooks and Bassano each have a primary feed mill to grind and blend barley, wheat, oats and corn into a variety of animal feeds. Together, these mills have a production capacity of over 3,200 tons (2,900 tonnes) per week, most of which is marketed in southeastern and central Alberta, or southwestern Saskatchewan.

A large, commercial beef processing and packing plant is located near Brooks. In a secondary operation, the hides are processed and made ready for tanning. Local abattoirs, or custom slaughterhouses, and butchers are situated in or near many of the communities, and cater to the demand for bulk freezer meats. Custom hanging and cutting of farmers' own beef and pork is the most important service, but some businesses also process big game shot by local hunters. Others sell meat, cut and wrapped, to local stores.

Inspecting pork carcasses.

Four seed-cleaning plants buy, clean and sell seed for local, domestic and foreign markets, with alfalfa seed accounting for the largest share of seed processed. Seed grains are also important, but the production of grass seed grown in the EID is negligible. One facility deals almost exclusively with pea, bean and other vegetable seed.

Those familiar prairie landmarks, the grain elevators, can be seen in most Eastern Irrigation District communities. The eleven that are still in service today represent a significant reduction from the seventeen that were in operation here in 1924. Within the past ten years, two local elevators have been phased out, in conjunction with the abandonment of rail lines to the hamlets of Gem and Scandia.

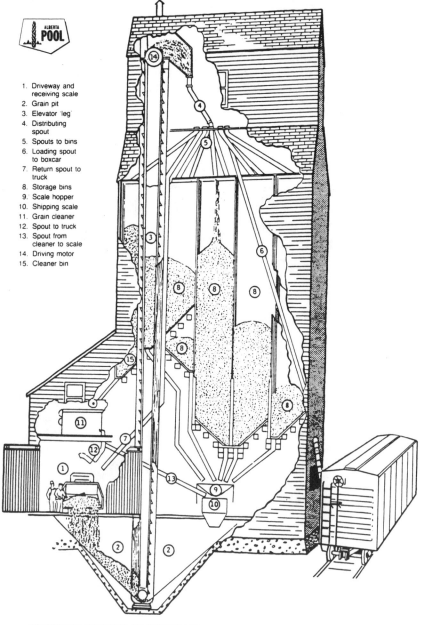

1. Driveway and receiving scale
2. Grain pit
3. Elevator 'leg'
4. Distributing spout
5. Spouts to bins
6. Loading spout to boxcar
7. Return spout to truck
8. Storage bins
9. Scale hopper
10. Shipping scale
11. Grain cleaner
12. Spout to truck
13. Spout from cleaner to scale
14. Driving motor
15. Cleaner bin

SCHEMATIC DRAWING TO ILLUSTRATE OPERATION OF COUNTRY ELEVATOR.

Although the number of elevators in the EID has decreased, the total amount of grain handled has increased over the years. Between 1960 and 1981, producer deliveries in this area increased by just over 40% — a rate considerably higher than the provincial average of 25.1%. The storage capacity of each elevator has also been enlarged, as original structures are replaced or fitted with additions. Currently, the eleven local elevators (two each in Bassano, Rosemary, Duchess and Tilley, and three in Brooks) have a total capacity of 997,140 bushels (27,170 metric tonnes). Alberta Wheat Pool's new high through-put elevator in Brooks has the largest single storage capacity: 176,000 bushels (4,800 tonnes) of wheat. It can handle 5,650 bushels (154 tonnes) of wheat per hour. From these facilities, most grain is shipped by rail cars to processing facilities or ports, but some also goes via truck to local feed mills.

AGRIBUSINESSES

Attached to the agricultural production and processing sectors is a thriving service industry, catering to the needs of farmers and ranchers. There are approximately ten businesses engaged in sales and maintenance of farm machinery, including irrigation pipes and sprinkler systems. Fertilizer and chemical herbicides and insecticides are primarily handled through grain elevators, but at least one chemical company has a fieldman resident in the EID, and available to provide sales information and advice to local consumers. Another important outlet for agricultural chemicals is provided by the numerous bulk dealers in the area, who also provide tanker service to deliver gasoline, diesel fuel and oil to farm locations.

Two livestock markets are located in Brooks; these provide local producers with a service for buying and selling their animals. Between them, they handled approximately 100,000 head of stock in 1983 — a fact which provides further clear evidence of the importance of livestock in the local economy.

The four veterinary clinics cater mainly to the needs of the many livestock producers located in the EID and its immediate vicinity; however, they also do small-animal work with cats and dogs.

Of course, many other types of businesses and services exist in the EID — each making its own contribution, and deriving benefits from its endeavours. Retail, professional and other services all provide employment for local residents, while profitting from the stability of the irrigation-based agricultural economy. Recent fluctuations in the petroleum industry have resulted in closures and cutbacks for many industries and services, but the relative stability of our agricultural sector has meant that a core of economic support is still available for most businesses in the area.

DOMESTIC AND MUNICIPAL WATER SUPPLIES

The Eastern Irrigation District, in addition to supplying water for irrigation purposes, also provides water for domestic and municipal use. Through a series of special rates and agreements, and aided by provincial grants, the District is contracted to convey water to all municipalities within its borders — the Towns of

Bassano and Brooks; the Villages of Duchess, Rosemary and Tilley; and, through the County of Newell, to the hamlets of Scandia, Patricia, Rolling Hills and Rainier. Other local residents are responsible for obtaining their own water from a centrally located standpipe supplied with filtered water from the irrigation system.

Commonplace on rural highways is the sight of farm trucks, loaded with large metal tanks, and dripping a steady stream of water. As the truck comes to a stop or turns a corner, water sloshes from the tank's opening and, in winter, quickly congeals into ice patches on the roadways. Once back home, the splashy cargo is discharged into a large underground storage tank, called a cistern, which is connected to the water pressure system. For those who lack the equipment and/or the motivation to haul their own water, a number of water hauling services run large-volume tanker trucks. These commercial vehicles can fill a cistern in one trip, saving the farmer the three or four trips necessary when using a small tank and truck.

In earlier days, the cisterns were filled to the brim every fall with irrigation water, just before the system was shut off. Filtered through sand or charcoal, the water would be eked out for household use over the winter, in the hope that it would last until spring when the canals were flowing again.

Some rural residents have constructed alternative storage facilities, in the form of large dug-outs, or reservoirs. These are filled each summer with water from the irrigation system. Before use, some households pass the water through a series of purification filters or inject it with chlorine.

Because virtually all water used within the bondaries of the EID is diverted from the Bow River, and because the same supply is used for all purposes — from human consumption, to stock watering, to sewage disposal — the quality of water is of concern to all District residents. So far, all local water users have co-operated to ensure that the quality of water meets, or exceeds, government standards for its various uses. Further co-operation is needed, however, among all communities that depend upon the Bow, in order to improve and maintain water quality for all users — both upstream and down.

INDUSTRIAL USES OF EID WATER

The largest single consumer of EID water is a water injection plant operated by a large oil and gas company. Located just west of Brooks, this facility pumps about 14,000 barrels (2,200 cubic metres) of water out of Lake Newell every day. This water is combined with the water which has been extracted, along with oil, from the producing wells. After going through a treatment process to remove most of the air, the water is injected back into the formation in sufficient volume to replace the extracted oil. This process ensures that underground pressures remain equalized, facilitating the effective recovery of oil from the other wells producing from the same strata.

Other industrial water users who purchase their supplies directly from the EID include oilfield trucking firms, Canadian Pacific Railway, vegetable and meat-packing plants, and a local apiary.

WATER-BASED OUTDOOR ACTIVITIES

PARKS IN THE EID

Water-based recreational opportunities in most of southeastern Alberta would be limited to the Bow, Red Deer and South Saskatchewan waterways were it not for the existence of irrigation reservoirs.

Kinbrook Island Provincial Park

Lake Newell, in addition to its role of storage reservoir for the EID, is also the site of Kinbrook Island Provincial Park, the major local outdoor recreation area. The isthmus on which the park is located was originally leased by the EID Board of Trustees to the Brooks Kinsmen Club in July of 1945. The service group began planting trees and otherwise improving the area. Then, after 1949, the Alberta Department of Public Works undertook all further development. Shortly thereafter, ownership and control of the 59-acre (24-ha) park was transferred by the EID to the Parks Board of Alberta Lands and Forests for the sum of one dollar.

J. L. Carroll Photographics Ltd.

Water-skiing has been popular at Lake Newell for over 35 years.

Today, this pleasant setting along the eastern shore of the lake offers boating, swimming and camping facilities. A summer village of privately-owned cottages extends along the shoreline for some distance.

Most park users are from the Brooks area, but visitors come from as far away as Medicine Hat and Calgary. Surveys show that rural residents make up a small proportion of the park users — probably, they're too busy irrigating!

Emerson Bridge Park

The County of Newell's Emerson Bridge Park is located just off Highway 36 where it crosses the Red Deer River. Named for George Emerson, an early rancher who lived nearby, the site is a popular spot for week-end outings. Camping, fishing and boating are available in the well-treed site on the river flat.

Tillebrook Provincial Park

PFRA.

Aerial view of campsite "wheels" at Tillebrook.

Although Tillebrook Provincial Park functions mainly as an overnight campsite for travellers along the Trans-Canada Highway, careful landscaping and the benefits of irrigation have been combined to create a well-equipped park in an attractive setting. Trees planted only a few years ago are already able to provide shade from the hot summer sun and shelter from the frequent strong winds — functions essential in a region that, like grasslands everywhere, is subject to climatic extremes.

Crawling Valley Recreation Area

In the northwest part of the EID, the only recreational opportunities available near water are limited to fishing and picnicking below Bassano Dam. This situation will be remedied in the near future when the large swimming, boating, picnicking and camping development at Crawling Valley Reservoir opens to the public.

Dinosaur Provincial Park

Although it is not directly involved with the irrigation system, Dinosaur Provincial Park offers considerable recreational opportunity within the District. Utilizing existing creek beds, two irrigation spillways meander through the park. From these, trees and lawns are irrigated to add to the beauty of the riverside setting. Since its designation as a UNESCO World Heritage Site in 1979, Dinosaur Park attracts more out-of-district, out-of-province and international visitors than any other local outdoor recreation area.

The awesomely dramatic, erratic badlands are a phenomenon dating back to the thawing of the Ice Age glaciers, 18,000 years ago. At that time, huge volumes of meltwaters rampaged along the route of the Red Deer River, gouging out the wide valley we see today. Gradually, the river calmed and was contained in its present channel. Its recession left behind a fantastic array of uniquely-shaped hills, battered into being by the erosive power of water.

The varicoloured strata of the badlands result from deposits laid down in the time, more than 75 million years ago, when dinosaurs ruled the land. The fossils of these fascinating beasts and their equally interesting fellow creatures are buried in the rock and, year by year, as erosion continues to alter the face of the landscape, skeletons emerge to tell the story of a very ancient time.

About 29 different species of dinosaur have so far been discovered in the park. Plant-eaters are the most numerous — the duck-billed Corythosaurus, the horned Centrosaurus and the tank-like Panoplosaurus are examples of these. They shared their world and provided a diet for the fierce meat-eaters — Albertosaurus and Stenonychosaurus are two of these. Skeletal traces of flying reptiles, giant marine reptiles, fish and the minute bones of primitive mammals are found along with those of the dinosaurs.

What emerges from the study of plant and animal fossils and from the sediments in which the skeletons are discovered is a picture of a very different world from the one we know in Alberta today. Then, it was a low-lying swampy plain covered in lush vegetation, coursed by many meandering rivers and lapped on the east by the waters of a large inland sea. The climate was sub-tropical and, as opposed to the water shortages we now know in this area, flooding by the sea was a frequent event, at least in geological time measurements. Dinosaur Provincial Park has the largest concentrated terrestrial fossil repository from Late Cretaceous times found in the world to date.

J. L. Carroll Photographics Ltd.

Badlands formations, Red Deer River valley, in 1947 — 8 years before Dinosaur Provincial Park established.

The fossil wealth of the park is its greatest asset, but it has other attractions to recommend it. There are archaeological remnants of cultures that thrived on the plains for thousands of years before the white man came on the scene. Dating of artifacts puts the earliest foot nomads in this part of the plains at least 11,000 years ago.

When the fur traders pushed their way, bit by bit, out into the great wilderness of the Northwest, they found an Indian population already possessed of horses. These animals had come northwards from South America and, as near as can be determined, arrived in this area about 1730. The fur trade was concentrated along the North Saskatchewan River and forays by traders onto the plains were infrequent. Until very late in the 19th century, the lands that are now southern Alberta were part of the great hunting grounds controlled by the Blackfoot, whose reputation as a warlike nation and whose total lack of interest in the trapping of beaver made the fur-trading companies reluctant to establish forts in their midst. Trading with the Blackfoot was done at the northern forts when the Indians brought buffalo meat, pemmican and skins to trade for guns, powder, beads and booze. Once the expansion of westward settlement began, the Indian tribes were relegated to reserves.

Arrow heads, tipi rings and cairns were plentiful on the prairie before the sod was turned. Even today, it is possible to stumble upon a site that has never before been recorded. More rare is evidence of the spiritual life of the ancestors of today's Indians. Within the park's boundaries is a wonderful stone effigy figure believed to have religious meaning. At another site, there is a "dream" bed, a rectangular rock structure set high on a mesa. It is thought that this shelter was used by an Indian man on a vision quest. To this remote spot, he would retreat to fast and pray for a vision to guide him throughout his life.

One piece of more recent local colour is embodied in the log cabin that stands near the entrance to the camping ground of the park. Snaked from the Red Deer River, logs used to construct the cabin were a bonanza that floated down from a break in a log boom upstream in the treed reaches of the river. The cabin was the home of John Ware, a rancher who, around the turn of the century, located with his family north of where Millicent is today. Ware was famous among the many outstanding men of the range — the Eide brothers, Rod McLeay, George Emerson, George Lane, Tom Owens, Paul Ryckman, Happy Jack Jackson, Jim Spratt, Gentleman Charlie Parks, Slim Woods, Mulligan Jack Thomas, Irish Bill McCarragher, Dick Imes, Chris Christianson, Charles Bray, the Douglasses, Peake brothers, Uncle Billy Caldwell and many more. John Ware, because of his great strength, his ability to ride out the meanest bronco, his decency and the fact that he was black, was a man among men.

The park preserves, free from harm, plant and animal life of our time, as well as of the ancient past. With conservation a primary aim of the staff, the park protects a wide range of indigenous prairie plants from the destruction that accompanies ranching and farming progress. Among the many interesting varieties are a number which are listed as endangered species.

If the stories of early ranchers in the area seem tinged with exaggeration when they pertain to the height of the grass in the years when this country was young, it is instructive to have a look at the isolated mesas in the park. Here, where there has been no grazing, the mid-grasses are truly of a height to "catch in the rowels of spurs," as one old timer phrased it. From the time of the last buffalo until the range was populated with cattle and horses, the grass grew undisturbed. The waving grasses on the park mesas give a picture in miniature of what our first settlers saw, a sea of prairie grass.

Interpretive trails and conducted bus tours in Dinosaur Provincial Park are designed to give the visitor an overall glance at some of the attractions in this unique badlands park.

SPORT FISHING

Sport fishing is a popular EID pastime, which without the stable water supply provided by the irrigation system would be severely limited. Pike, perch, whitefish, walleye, rainbow trout and ling ply the waters of Lake Newell and a number of other large reservoirs.

Anglers are presented with the chance to hook a trout in several man-made ponds. These are stocked through the auspices of Alberta Energy and Natural Resources, Fish and Wildlife Division.

The winners! Lake Newell, 1963.

COMMERCIAL FISHERIES

Lake Newell, Cowoki Lake, Tilley B and Rolling Hills reservoirs are among those fished commercially every year. Whitefish is the most important species, as it has a ready market and commands a good price. At present, EID reservoirs produce 40 per cent of the total catch of lake whitefish in southern Alberta. Pike, suckers, trout and walleye are caught occasionally.

Because these are all man-made reservoirs, the fish stocks now present in them were transplanted from other areas. For instance, the whitefish swimming in Lake Newell are descendants of stock hatched from five million eggs brought from lakes in northern Alberta. These eggs were placed in Lake Newell in April of 1932 through the efforts of R. T. Todd, Director of Fisheries for Alberta, and Gus Griffin of the CPR.

Commercial fishing is done mainly during the winter months in southern Alberta. Fishermen simply drive out over the ice to where the waters are deep, cut two large holes, and string a gill net out under the ice between the two holes. Cool temperatures, both in the water and up above, ensure good quality fish. In recent years, Lake Newell was designated a summer fishery. Fishermen now go out in boats just after the ice breaks up in the spring. As part of an overall fish management program, Alberta Energy and Natural Resources sets quotas, and regulates the number of nets and mesh size allowed for each lake.

EID winter fishery has been ongoing for over 50 years.

When commercial fishing first began here, some people spent all winter moving around and fishing lakes throughout the province. By working hard and travelling far, they were able to support themselves and their families during the winter months. Then, they would look for other work to provide a summer livelihood. Today, most of those who engage in commercial fishing regard it as a welcome source of supplemental income.

In the 1983-84 season, the total catch from EID reservoirs was 225,712 pounds (102,597 kg). Of this amount, almost 92 per cent was whitefish. The single largest proportion of the catch (34 per cent) came from Tilley B Reservoir.

Until recently, most local fish was sold to wholesalers, who then distributed it to retail outlets across the West. In 1983, the federal government's Fresh Water Fish Marketing Corporation opened an agency in the Brooks Industrial Park. Some fishermen now take their catch to this outlet, which has facilities for weighing, cleaning, packing and storing fish on the premises. Fish processed by the government agency are shipped to Winnipeg for marketing.

WATERFOWL

Ducks Unlimited is a private, non-profit, international organization engaged in conservation, restoration and development of waterfowl habitat. For over 40 years, Ducks Unlimited Canada has worked in the Eastern Irrigation District. The first project constructed in the Brooks area was Lake San Francisco (Cassils Lake), which was completed in 1942. Since then, through the co-operation of landowners and the EID, DU has developed more than 75 projects. Tilley A (Campbell Reservoir), Louisiana Lakes, Kininvie Lakes, Will J. Reid, and Kitsim are some of these. Private landowners sign easements to make their land available for the projects; DU provides the funding, personnel and expertise to complete and maintain the sites; and the EID supplies the water.

It is apparent how important southern Alberta is as a breeding ground for ducks and geese when one considers that 65 per cent of all North American waterfowl is raised on the Canadian prairies. Permanent habitat has been established for the birds in the Brooks area by the building of extensive networks of reservoirs and ponds to create the marshlands they favour.

Ducks Unlimited Canada.

Mallard duck and her brood, Kitsim Project.

Display of ducks and geese shot in early days at Tilley.

The EID is located in both the Pacific and Central Flyways; so, large numbers of ducks and geese migrate through the area each fall. The wetlands attract the birds; and the birds, in turn, attract both local and non-resident hunters.

Over the last decade, the populations of most species of ducks and geese have been declining steadily. An exception is the Canada goose. The goose population within the EID is so plentiful and stable that Alberta Fish and Wildlife and Ducks Unlimited have instituted a transplant program. Geese migrate back to nest on water where they learned to fly. By trapping goslings still in the nest, and transplanting them each year in July, from the Brooks area to other suitable locations throughout the province, the geographical distribution of the Alberta goose population has been greatly extended.

UPLAND GAME BIRDS AND BROOKS WILDLIFE CENTRE

Two exotic varieties of imported game birds have become so well-established in southern Alberta that they have virtually replaced the native sharp-tailed grouse and prairie chicken. One of these species, the Chinese ring-necked pheasant, has become strongly identified with our region. It is prominently displayed on the crests of both the County of Newell and the Town of Brooks. Less well-known is the European grey, or Hungarian, partridge.

Although pheasants were originally introduced into Alberta by a group of Calgary sportsmen in 1908, rearing and release of the birds did not begin in Brooks until almost 20 years later. In 1925, Ralph Baird was assistant superintendent of the CPR's Irrigation Invesstigation Branch at Brooks. One of his duties was to supervise the Brooks Demonstration Farm. He was also secretary-treasurer of the Brooks Fish and Game Association. In these dual capacities, Baird was responsible for importing 100 pheasant eggs from California, which were then hatched and reared in captivity. The raising of pheasants was treated like any other experiment in livestock breeding at the farm, and various methods of incubation and combinations of feed rations were tested.

These early efforts at pheasant propagation were, in the main, successful. When the project was threatened by the depletion of the Fish and Game Association's small treasury, personal funds from a number of concerned individuals and corporate backing from the CPR ensured its continuation. Within one year after the pheasant rearing program was undertaken at the Demonstration Farm, several locals began to hatch and release birds from their own farms, thereby establishing the pheasant population over a wider geographical area.

Pheasant propagation in Alberta continued on this small scale until 1934, when the Provincial Game Commissioner arranged to obtain 450 adult birds from South Dakota. In exchange, Alberta was to provide an equal number of Hungarian partridge. Also introduced to the Calgary area in 1908, the "Hun" had become well-established throughout the province within a few years, making the South Dakota order easy to fill. Three hundred of the pheasants obtained in this trade were released in the Brooks area, and provided parent stock to enhance the existing local release programs.

In the decade following the formation of the Eastern Irrigation District, there was little organized bird culture. Then, in 1945, the provincial government's Department of Lands and Mines established the Pheasant Hatchery in Brooks.

J. L. Carroll Photographics Ltd.

Products of Provincial Pheasant Hatchery, Brooks, 1950.

Brooks Bulletin.

Pheasant release program, Brooks Wildlife Centre.

Fittingly, this facility was located on what had been CPR Demonstration Farm property, just east of the town. The hatchery annually produced about 1,200 young birds for release. All eggs hatched during the first six years of operation were supplied by local school children, who were paid a shiny nickel for each egg they collected from the wild.

By 1952, the hatchery had outgrown itself and was relocated to a larger parcel of land on the western edge of Brooks. Annual pheasant production increased over the years, reaching the 10,000 mark in 1965.

When the second ten-year lease on this location expired in 1972, the EID requested that the hatchery make plans to relocate. The growth of Brooks dictated that such a central site should be redeveloped for other uses more appropriate to an urban setting. Renamed the Brooks Wildlife Centre, the present facility is located on a 346-acre (140-ha) site east of Brooks, just off the Trans-Canada Highway. It was officially opened in 1978.

Billed as the largest and most up-to-date wildlife propagation facility in Canada, the Centre has an annual egg production capacity of 200,000 with brooding and rearing houses for up to 100,000 pheasants. Facilities capable of producing 500 to 600 young Canada geese for transplant into habitat development areas in Alberta; waterfowl propagation and research capabilities; indoor and outdoor raptor facilities large enough to maintain up to 70 injured birds of prey; and a major area for Japanese quail propagation (undertaken to meet food requirements of the animals and birds housed at Brooks and at its sister-operation in Wainwright) were developed at the new site. A well-equipped laboratory to aid in effective disease control for wildlife throughout the southern portion of the province rounds out the Centre's comprehensive contribution to wildlife management in Alberta. Interpretive programs are offered to the public from April through August.

BIG GAME

Pronghorn antelope, white-tailed deer and mule deer are the major big game species native to the Eastern Irrigation District. Small herds of pronghorn may be seen grazing on open prairie areas where sage, their staple food, is plentiful. These small animals are tan in colour with white cheeks. White and dark tan slashes pattern their throats. Known for their fleetness — they have been clocked at speeds of up to 62 miles (100 km) per hour — antelope can zip under fence wires without seeming to slow down. Despite the expansion of agricultural land use, enough native grasslands remain to support a good number of antelope.

Named for their large, perked-up ears, mule deer are common in many different habitats throughout the District — on the open prairie, among the trees and willows of the ditchbanks, and in the coulees and river valleys. It is lovely to see the graceful syncopated movement of a herd of running mule deer, looking for all the world like merry-go-round steeds.

Unlike the mule deer, the white-tailed, or flag-tailed, deer seldom leave the densely wooded areas. When startled, this species raises its short white tail as a warning (or flag) to its fellows, before silently and swiftly disappearing into the

Brooks & District Museum.

For many years, Charlie "The Wolfer" Blazier raised antelope for sale to zoos and game farms.

trees. White-tails seldom venture from the protection of the Red Deer River valley, and the coulees which lead into it.

In addition to the many farmers and ranchers who enjoy the hunt, local townsfolk, and people from the Lethbridge, Medicine Hat and Calgary areas flock to the District to pursue their quarry — for the sport of it, for the taste of wild game and, for the lucky few, the trophy.

Although it is not of major economic importance, a significant number of local residents supplement their income by trapping. The EID staff often find that their work has been sabotaged by beaver and muskrat whose lodges block the water flow in canals. When this happens they are quick to give permission to local licensed trappers to remove the offending little beasts.

Coyotes and foxes inhabit both cultivated areas and grasslands. During hunting season, a few locals can sometimes add to their cashflow by trapping or shooting these canines, and then selling the hides for use as fur collars and coats. Other species trapped for fur are mink, badger and cottontail rabbit.

The foregoing section details the benefits of irrigation which we enjoy in 1985: prosperous communities, consistently high levels of agricultural production, a thriving service sector, and fine recreational opportunities.

The fabric of life for the 17,500 residents of the EID is interwoven with irrigation. Everywhere apparent are the values it has bestowed upon this patch of prairie.

From our vantage point in the present, it seems obvious that irrigation was the salvation of what must otherwise have remained an under-populated expanse of barren land. But, as we shall see in the pages to follow, the evolution of our area, as it has taken place, was far from foreordained. A large element of chance hovered over events in our past history. Only gradually did the architects of westward expansion accept the building of irrigation systems as a necessary step in the foundation of a firm agricultural base on the dry plains of southern Alberta.

PART II
BACKGROUND TO THE
FORMATION OF THE EID

Elaborate display by CPR Department of Natural Resources at an exhibition in Chicago, promoting Western Canada. Framed map in background shows developments in the Bow Valley irrigation block.

EARLY ASSESSMENTS OF THE NORTHWEST

In 1870, when the newly-born Dominion of Canada achieved the transfer of Rupert's Land from the Hudson Bay Company, she was taking unto herself a great unknown quantity. The National Dream of Sir John A. Macdonald's government called for intensive settlements linked by transcontinental rail. At the time of Confederation, the furthest west agricultural settlement was the Red Deer River colony on the site of present-day Winnipeg. Beyond this tiny outpost of civilization, as far as the natural barrier of the Rocky Mountains, stretched 800 miles (1,300 km) of prairie wilderness. It was the preserve of nomadic tribes of Indians, Metis buffalo hunters and a handful of white fur traders and missionaries.

What was known of the resources that might support settlement came from fur trader-explorers' accounts and from two extensive reconnaissance surveys carried out in the late 1850's. At that time, impelled by fears that American annexationists were casting covetous eyes northward to British territory, and reacting to the expressed desire of what was then the colony of Canada to extend itself to the Pacific Ocean, the British government was prompted to finance an expedition to examine the prospects for Rupert's Land, or the Northwest, as it was more commonly known.

The British North American Exploring Expedition, under the direction of an adventurous Irishman, Captain John Palliser, lasted from 1857 through 1860. Palliser and his team of men, who were trained in geology, botany and meteorology, travelled over thousands of miles from Lake Superior through Kicking Horse Pass, mapping and recording their observations.

In the same years that Palliser's group was criss-crossing the Northwest, the Red River and Assiniboine Exploring Expedition under H. Y. Hind, a Toronto naturalist and geologist, and Simon T. Dawson, a surveyor, was fielded by Canada. This expedition was charged to determine "the best route for opening a facile communication through British territory from [Lake Superior] to the Red River Settlement and ultimately to the great tracts of cultivable land beyond them." Their investigations did not reach into Alberta but explored as far west as the Qu'Appelle River Valley and the country upstream of the elbow of the South Saskatchewan River.

Voluminous reports issued from these expeditions and added greatly to the scientific knowledge of the interior. Although recommendations following from the reports differed in some respects — chiefly on the advisability of building an all-Canadian rail system — they were agreed on the agricultural potential offered by what are now Alberta and Saskatchewan. A "Fertile Belt" lying along the North Saskatchewan River was identified as the most preferable agricultural land. It was advised that settlement of the area lying to the south of this rich land should be avoided.

Assessment of the worth of the southern region was founded on the belief that it was an extension of the "Great American Desert," a geographical concept common at the time in both the United States and Canada. Hind's perception of its northern limits closely parallels that of Palliser. The latter drew a description of a rough triangular area with its base the international boundary between longitudes 100 degrees and 114 degrees and its apex reaching to the 52nd parallel. This is Palliser's description of the country in which the Eastern Irrigation District lies:

> The South Saskatchewan, which in its upper part is called Bow River, . . . flows in a deep and narrow valley, through a region of arid plains, devoid of timber or pasturage of good quality . . . The sage and the cactus abound and the whole of the scanty vegetation bespeaks an arid climate.

To this day, the area Palliser described as infertile is known as Palliser's Triangle. His name and his judgement have since been castigated in the light of the bountiful harvests this region has subsequently produced.

In his defense, it should be said that the appraisal by Palliser and his associates was not categorically negative. Dr. James Hector, the Scottish geologist attached to the expedition, stated that the triangle contained "many varieties of land and some limited areas that are really even good." Eyes accustomed to the verdant growth of the British Isles must have registered the prairies as bleak and barren indeed. Often, experience bore out their initial perceptions. Travelling from the Hand Hills to the confluence of the Red Deer and South Saskatchewan Rivers, for example, the party had trouble locating sufficient water and grass for their horses. Dry farming methods were still to be developed and the idea of irrigating millions of acres of prairie was almost as remote from consideration in the 1850's as emigrating to Mars is in our day. It is not really surprising that, in general, they judged the area as not desirable for settlement. Certainly, their opinions were endorsed by the hundreds of farmers who "starved out" in the Triangle of the Depression's dust-bowl years.

Overland emigration to the western United States in the 1840's and 50's gradually dispelled the myth of the "Great American Desert." Experience taught that the actual desert occupied but a small part of the total area. The myth died a slow death but when it was finally laid to rest, there arose in its stead, on both sides of the border, an equally extreme, if quite opposite image — that of a veritable Garden of Eden.

Once the Dominion of Canada assumed responsibility for the adminstration of the Northwest, events that were to shape our nation moved rapidly. British Columbia entered confederation in 1871 on the express condition that it would be linked to the rest of Canada by rail. Building the railway and settling the west were the twin planks of government policy and each was pursued with vigour.

The decision to build a transcontinental railway was taken by Parliament in 1871 but the "Pacific Scandal," a political patronage issue, brought the Conservative government down two years later. Then, a world-wide economic slump interfered with the succeeding Liberal government's plans to get a railway started. Together, these factors caused a delay of ten years before construction began.

The CPR was begun in 1881 under an agreement between John A. Macdonald's Conservatives, once more in power, and the CPR Syndicate. The railway company was to receive $25 million and 25 million acres (10,125,000 ha) of land, made up of the odd-numbered sections in a 24-mile-wide (39-km-wide) belt on either side of the rail line, in return for building 1,900 miles (3,060 km) of rail from Lake of the Woods to Craigellachie.

CPR train of 1885 vintage, used in filming "The National Dream" near Cassils, 1973.
Photographer: S. Alberts.

There were two hitches to carrying out the land subsidy section of this agreement, both of which were factors leading to the development of the CPR Irrigation Block in Alberta. In the first place, not all of the land through which the rail line passed was Canada's to give. Lands contiguous to the main line in Ontario, British Columbia and most of Manitoba were already owned and settled. The payment in land came almost completely from the Northwest, now the provinces of Alberta and Saskatchewan. Consequently, there was not enough land, in the alternate sections of the 48-mile-wide (77-km-wide) belt through which the railway ran, to meet the commitment. Northern Reserves were established in the Northwest to make up the shortfall.

The building of the railway was of such importance to the young Dominion of Canada that it was seen as a good buy at almost any price. Land grants for the establishment of transportation networks had a considerable history in the United States, with both good and bad results. Although the Conservatives and Liberals quibbled about details, they both accepted a transplant of the American policy to Canada. Land was the one seemingly unlimited commodity in the Northwest when Canada took it over from the Hudson Bay Company. Trading it for railways was seen as the only practical course to follow in pursuit of the public interest.

There was a second factor in the land subsidy deal which had a direct bearing on the irrigation block. This was the "fairly fit for settlement" clause, which stipulated that the company was not bound to accept any of the alternate sections along its line that did not meet this requirement. Acting on this right, the CPR rejected all of the land available to it along the stretch of rail from Moose Jaw to the Rocky Mountains.

These were the great days of surveys: the Dominion Land Survey, the Boundary Commission Survey, the Canadian Pacific Railway Survey, and the Geological Survey of Canada, all contributed to the growing mass of data on the

Canadian west. Report followed report and, in theory, should have rendered settlement policies eminently rational. What seems to have happened, in fact, is that the rhapsodic boosterism of one surveyor swayed the politicians of the day away from the measured judgements of several others.

John Macoun was a botany teacher in Belleville, Ontario when he chanced to meet Sandford Fleming. Impressed with Macoun's knowledge, Fleming, the chief surveyor for the CPR, became his mentor. Survey jobs with the CPR, special assignments for the Department of the Interior and, ultimately, employment as a naturalist with the Geological Survey of Canada followed. Critics of Macoun point out that he had not ventured south of the South Saskatchewan River when, in 1880, he reported on the total area north of the U.S. boundary and south of latitude 51 degrees, between Manitoba and the Rocky Mountains. In this region of over 90,000 square miles (233,100 sq km), he considered only 19,000 (49,210 sq km) square miles as arid or sandy. Other historians have charged that he was pleading the special interests of the railway syndicate which was determined to abandon the originally-proposed northern route of the CPR for a more southerly one. However, it is likely that factors other than agricultural settlement possibilities determined the eventual route of the line through the comparatively arid lands of the southern prairies. Cheaper construction costs and a desire to prevent railway interests in the United States from draining off traffic from Canada were persuasive considerations.

Whatever his reasons, Macoun virtually reversed the recommendations of others and was at pains to discredit Palliser. In his popular book, *Manitoba and the Great North-West*, published in 1882, he went so far as to argue that "the absence of water is a good sign on the prairie" and that a practical farmer would select the sparsely vegetated prairie rather than land that must be cleared of brush before ploughing and seeding could begin. This is to suggest that, for agricultural settlement, Palliser's Triangle was to be preferred to his Fertile Belt.

The policies pursued by the Dominion government in populating the West imply that Macoun's words were heeded. How else could one explain homesteads being offered on the millions of acres of grassland now administered as Special Areas in Alberta?

Other surveyors of the day qualified some of the conclusions reached by Palliser and his contemporaries, but their comments tended to be more conservative than those of Macoun. G. M. Dawson was one of these. Dawson joined the Boundary Commission as a young geologist. Later, he directed intensive geological investigation of various regions of the West, including the Bow and Belly River Regions. He was appointed director of the Geological Survey of Canada in 1895. Obviously, as a geologist, he was interested in more than just the surface of the earth. From an agricultural point of view, the ability of sub-soils to conserve moisture may be as important as the character of the top soil. Dawson was the first to take this into account when judging arability of the land. He cautioned that much of the southern prairie consisted of light soils and sub-soils and, considering the scant rainfall, would not retain sufficient water for the growth of anything but the native short grasses. Excellent pastures they were and should remain, he advised.

IRRIGATION IS INTRODUCED

Perhaps Dawson was also the first to mention irrigation with respect to this semi-arid country; however, he did not consider it a practical solution to the lack of moisture. He believed that the gorges in which prairie rivers ran were so deep as to make it impossible for their waters to be applied at prairie level.

Irrigation was not a popular idea in the early days of western settlement. As the steel track stretched further and further onto the plain, it brought with it a vanguard of pioneer ranchers and farmers. The tent town of Medicine Hat, set up in 1883 as a camp for railway workers, grew quickly and, by 1887, was a thriving little community. Lethbridge was the metropolis of the southern prairie founded on rich coal deposits in its environs. When the rail reached Calgary, settlers began to cluster around the Northwest Mounted Police Fort, setting up businesses to cater to the ranching interests that were moving in to take advantage of the fine grasslands. In the optimism of the frontier heyday, any hint that the country needed irrigation was viewed as idle rumour-mongering that would stem the flow of immigration. The years of 1883 and 1884 were wet. Some stands of oats in the Medicine Hat district were reported to be of a height to conceal a standing man. That seemed proof enough that to reap its rewards farmers had but to break up and seed the land.

Talk of irrigation was in the interests of neither the CPR nor the government. Rapid settlement was projected to recoup the heavy investments they had sunk into railway construction, but after an initial boom, immigration on the anticipated scale failed to materialize. To have it become known that the land along the rail line was dry would only exacerbate the problem of attracting immigrants.

Undaunted by the negative reception of his ideas, one man continued to press home his conviction that settlement of the prairie without irrigation was folly. That man was William Pearce, who has since been dubbed the "Father of Irrigation." As a surveyor, Pearce had gained a good deal of knowledge of the West. In 1882, when the Dominion Lands Board was created to administer homestead lands, Pearce was appointed Inspector of Lands Agencies and based in Winnipeg. Travelling to Calgary by rail in 1883, he struck up an acquaintance with a man from Colorado, who was familiar with irrigation in that state. His travelling companion remarked on how productive the country they were travelling through could be, if only the Bow River were flowing out onto it. This conversation seems to have focussed Pearce's interest on irrigation and he began to study its effects in the western United States and its feasibility for the Canadian Northwest.

Pearce was a man of boundless energy and enthusiasm. He was known far and wide across the West. He learned about the problems facing the new settler, not from reports written for him by others, but by long days on the trail. He carried a bedroll and slept out in the open when lodging was not at hand. In his travels, he talked with everyone he met.

There are recollections by pioneers of the Eastern Irrigation District, preserved in the Glenbow Museum Archives, which give some measure of this man. W. Tait White, an early settler instrumental in the formation of the EID, remembers Pearce's indefatigable endurance. He was able to walk further and faster in a

William Pearce at work in his CPR office, 1914.

day than most men could travel on horseback. White called Pearce a "horse of a man." Charlie Chalmers, who later spent many years in Brooks with Grimm Alfalfa Seed Growers Ltd., worked for Pearce as a driver before World War I. Their trips together took them over much of southern Alberta, where Pearce was studying the geology for indications of oil. Bouncing over rough trails in a Model "T" Ford from dawn to dusk was endured equally well by the young chauffeur and his 70-year-old passenger. Nothing stood in the way of Pearce's investigations, neither a river bridge washed out nor a barbed wire fence. Encountering the first, he directed Chalmers to drive on through the river. Coming upon the second, in the absence of gates on a trail he had selected, Pearce simply jumped out of the car and cut the wires.

When Pearce first began to promote irrigation, he was stifled by his superiors in Ottawa. But it was not too long before Nature rallied support for his cause. In the mid-1880's, drought set in and, by 1890, it had become an acute problem. Local newspapers, which earlier had scoffed, now began to agitate for irrigation. Groups were organized to persuade the government to undertake large irrigation schemes in the West.

As the settlers' plight worsened and recognition of the basic cause of their distress became unavoidable, the government took action. In 1892, Pearce was asked to draft proposals concerning government responsibility for the regulation and administration of water resources in the Northwest. His colleague, J. S. Dennis, Jr., who was the Chief Inspector of Surveys for the Department of the Interior, requested the assignment of studying irrigation law and practice in the western United States. A draft bill, drawn up by the two men, was circulated to interested parties in the Northwest, who agreed with its intent. In 1894, the Northwest Irrigation Act was passed unanimously by the Parliament of Canada.

As in so many aspects of westward expansion, Canada took lessons from her American cousins. In the case of irrigation law, she learned from problems that had arisen in the western states where irrigation was practiced. Dennis estimated that, in the United States, there was as much money spent on litigation over irrigation matters as there was on constructing the water systems. The difficulty was something known in English Common Law as riparian rights. This principle allows for the free use of water by all those who own land along its shores. When this law was freely applied in the U.S., diversions of river flow for private irrigation schemes often deprived those further downstream of water. Lawsuits resulted.

The Northwest Irrigation Act of 1894 averted these sorts of problems in Canada. As in the case of the Northwest Mounted Police, who were here to administer the law in advance of settlement, irrigation law was in place before large-scale projects were begun. Ownership of water resources was vested in the Crown, riparian rights of individuals were suppressed, and a licensing system for the use of water was instituted.

To implement the law, it was necessary to know the extent of water resources and how best those might be used to irrigate the most suitable land and benefit the largest number of people. J. S. Dennis was put in charge of the Irrigation Surveys Branch of the Department of the Interior. Established in Calgary the year the law was passed, this division was responsible for taking the water inventory and dealing with applications for license to irrigate.

Public pressure on the government to encourage the development of large irrigation schemes intensified in the 1890's. Local newspapers, *The Medicine Hat Times* and *The Lethbridge Herald*, mounted steady editorial campaigns arguing the need for irrigation. They castigated the government for dragging its feet on the issue, and thereby retarding the settlement of the Northwest.

With the enactment of the Act in 1894, the government had endorsed the desirability of irrigation but it was not prepared to assume the considerable expense of actually implementing it. The alternative was to attract private investment — and what more likely target than the CPR? It had as big a stake in settling the west as did the government.

Pearce had been actively promoting the feasibility of irrigating from the Bow River for many years, both to his superiors in the Department of the Interior and to officials of the CPR. Part of his duties with the Lands Agency Board of the Department of the Interior included overseeing the selection of land for the pay-out of the CPR subsidy. This led to his close association with employees of that company. An 1894 report prepared by A. M. Burgess, Deputy Minister of the Interior, and William Pearce, stated that "there are large areas in the region [between Medicine Hat and the 5th Principal Meridian] which could be satisfactorily and profitably irrigated by the waters of the Bow River . . . and about three million acres could thus be reclaimed from comparative aridity and rendered productive for all purposes of mixed farming.'' The report goes on to say that to encourage irrigation projects, it would be necessary to abandon the government's original plan of payment to the railway — this being the allotment of alternate sections along the main rail line. It was considered unlikely that a private firm could be persuaded to invest in an irrigation system unless it owned all the lands watered by it. From this reasonable assumption, the block system of land grants evolved.

Ironically, the CPR had invoked the "fairly fit for settlement" clause to refuse the alternate sections contiguous to the rail line between Moose Jaw and Calgary, and demanded a substitution for these acres in a more humid area. Early attempts to prove the possibility of dry farming in this stretch of the prairie had failed. In the early 1880's, the CPR established experimental farms west of Swift Current. At that time, a wet cycle produced creditable crops and encouraged the Dominion and the CPR to jointly undertake the settlement of a German colony at Dunsmore, just east of Medicine Hat. The return of dry years in the mid-1880's destroyed this farming endeavour in its infancy. Disappointment at the results of this and similar ventures convinced the CPR that attempts to convert this land to something other than a cattle range were doomed to failure. Now, the possibility that irrigation might render a transformation that would attract settlers and, therefore, generate traffic for the railway far beyond what it could expect from the ranching industry, cast a new light on the entire situation. The company entered into negotiations with the government.

The way of the future had been pointed out by a small group of Latter-day Saints, experienced irrigationists from Utah, who came to the Cardston area in 1887 with the purpose of settling on irrigable land. By 1896, they were irrigating from the St. Mary River on a small scale. Other private irrigation schemes in Alberta, while they showed limited success, were ultimately hampered by the lack of capital necessary to build and maintain enduring structures.

The first corporate investment was undertaken by the Galt business conglomerate, which planned to extend the system the Mormons had initiated. Clifford Sifton, famous for advances in western settlement while he was Minister of the Interior, had come to office with the Laurier Liberals in 1896. He was eager to assist this entrepreneurial foray into irrigation. Accordingly, he allowed the company to consolidate its considerable land holding, earned from the building of a railway line linking Lethbridge and its coal mines with the main line of the CPR, into blocks convenient for irrigation. The government also reimbursed the survey costs and assisted in the sales promotions of the lands. The Alberta Irrigation Company, later reorganized as the North West Irrigation Company, provided the capital. Mormon settlers supplied the labour, in exchange for cash and land. Water was flowing in the canals by 1899.

Meanwhile, the CPR was becoming more amenable to the government's urging that it enter the irrigation arena. Before committing itself, however, and in spite of numerous government and railway surveys already on file, the company insisted upon an independent feasibility study. The government sought the opinion of a noted irrigation specialist from Colorado, George Anderson, who was employed as the chief engineer on the St. Mary project. Following his survey of the Bow River basin area in 1901, he gave assurance that Pearce's scheme was workable.

By the turn of the century, with improving world economic conditions, the pace of immigration stepped up. A number of factors, among them the development of hardy strains of wheat, a rising demand and price for grain, and improved dry farming methods, contributed to a rush of landseekers. Homestead lands in the United States had run out and the Canadian West became increasingly attractive to prospective farmers.

It was now 15 years since the main line of the CPR had been completed. The "fairly fit for settlement" stipulation had proved to be a thorny obstacle to completing the agreement between the government and the CPR. It allowed the railway company to reject a good deal of the land offered it. In 1900, there still remained over three million acres (1,215,000 ha) outstanding in the government debt to the company. It was imperative that the land subsidy be paid out before it became further complicated by the settlement process.

Animosity towards the CPR was intense at the turn of the century, especially in the West. The conviction that the price the builders of the railroad had exacted from the country was too high and that the West had been exploited for the gains of an eastern company took root and has never really been shaken. The results in immigration were disappointing. It had been thought that a railway was all that was needed to bring a flood of settlers to Canada. However, in 1895, a full decade after the last spike had been driven, the population of the entire Northwest was only 66,000. The Liberal party had never been as close to the CPR as their Conservative counterparts were. When they came to power in 1896, they thought it in their best political interest to close out the agreement between Canada and the CPR as expeditiously as possible. They set the final date for selection of the remaining land payment at June of 1904. Any outstanding claims from the CPR after that date would not be honoured.

The CPR's option of negotiating for land far from its rail system in the more humid regions of the Northwest was weighed against the capital expenditures necessary to make the semi-arid block produce the desired freight revenues for its main line. The die was cast for the CPR irrigation scheme when the company accepted a three-million-acre (1,215,000 ha), 48-mile-wide (77-km-wide) block of land between Calgary and Medicine Hat, along with 800,000 acres (324,000 ha) in the Northern Reserve, as the final installment of the many millions of acres awarded it for the building of the main line of its railroad.

The year was 1903. In this vast tract of land, there was but one trace of civilization on the rail line between Medicine Hat and Calgary. This was a livestock shipping point at Gleichen. The country was wide-open pasture held on lease from the Department of the Interior by cattle and horse ranchers. Irrigation spelled doom to the free-ranging life of the cowboy. The CPR continued to grant the leasing of the land but it was only a matter of time before settlers would come with their fences and their plows, to alter for all time the character of the short-grass prairie between the Red Deer and the Bow.

THE CPR'S IRRIGATION BLOCK

To the CPR, irrigation was a means to an end — that being the assurance of permanent settlement of the semi-arid lands of the prairie and the resulting rail traffic. Having accepted the principle that irrigation was the way to accomplish its aim, the company was energetic in launching the building of the water system. The best people available were hired. J. S. Dennis was lured away from the government service in 1902 to organize the CPR Irrigation Branch. Like his father before him, Dennis had been a distinguished land surveyor. In the very earliest years of settlement in the West, he worked for both the Dominion government and the Hudson Bay Company. During the Riel Rebellion in 1885, as Captain Dennis, he commanded the Dominion Land Surveyors' Intelligence Corps, popularly known as "Dennis's Scouts." The rank of Colonel, with which he was frequently addressed, was earned with the reserve forces.

Glenbow Archives.

John Stoughton Dennis, Jr., 1914.

Dennis's contribution to the development of the irrigation block was of overriding importance. Later, when the CPR Department of Natural Resources was founded in 1912, Dennis became its first manager. In this job, he was instrumental in shaping the colonization policies that guided the railway company in its settlement of the West.

Pearce, who had been so persuasive a promoter of the CPR venture into irrigation, joined the railway company in 1904. Although he held several important positions during his 26-year association with the CPR, his intimate involvement with the irrigation project on the Bow was over. It was the broader scope of irrigation that caught Pearce's imagination. Detailed project planning held less appeal for him.

Preliminary surveys for the project had been conducted by government surveyors in 1894 when serious negotiations with the CPR first got underway. Their evaluation of the topography vis-à-vis its adaptation to a gravity irrigation system was exceedingly optimistic. They proposed that a diversion of the Bow River near Calgary could provide water to two million acres (810,000 ha) and, through the channels of old coulees and stream beds, could extend as far east as Medicine Hat. George Anderson, the consultant engineer hired by the government at the CPR's request, had concurred with this plan.

Subsequent detailed surveys by CPR engineers ruled out its feasibility, however. They showed that the area naturally divided into three sections. These were designated as Western, Central and Eastern. Only the Western Section could be adequately served from the intake near Calgary. The Central Section was deemed non-irrigable because of its rough terrain, and plans were made to market it as dry land.

Building of the Western Section was tackled first. By 1910, construction was complete, the system was in operation, and two-thirds of the land had been sold. The staff of the Irrigation Branch now turned its attention to the Eastern Section.

Construction brought a boom to the area. The population of Bassano spiked to over 1,200 persons in the seasons of high construction activity at the diversion dam on the Bow. On May 26, 1911, *The Bassano News* reported that "500 men are employed around the dam." The pay list of two of the larger camps was said to amount to $2,000 a day. Of the more unusual imports to the work force that year were 400 teams of mules from Panama.

Cookhouse gathering of CPR fencing crew and visitors from nearby 3V ranch. Near Bassano, 1910.

Every spring was a time of excitement in Bassano, as "merchants look forward to solid business being better than ever." In the inimitable words of W. B. Cameron, editor of *The Bassano News*, "all the preliminary symptoms of briskness to come are on hand."

As work on the dam neared completion, the pace of life in Bassano slowed. When building of the Brooks Aqueduct began, the population explosion was propelled eastward. The number of inhabitants in one village after another in the Eastern Section was temporarily expanded as surveyors, followed by work crews, proceeded with the extension of the canal system.

It took only four years to complete the building of what, in its time, was described as the largest irrigation project on the North American continent. By 1914 water was flowing in the ditches. All that the region lacked was people, as Sir William Van Horne, president of the CPR, said, to "make the prairie fairly stink with blossoms."

Friendly chat at CPR Commissariat Brooks, 'Teens.

Glenbow Archives.

Part of workforce on irrigation project, Bassano, 1913.

The Archives, Sir Alexander Galt Museum.

SETTLEMENT IN THE EASTERN SECTION

The CPR was no stranger to land promotion. Almost as soon as the railroad was begun, the company assembled its advertising organization. A sophisticated network of agents was set up to reach into all corners of the globe from which immigration was likely or desirable — Great Britain, the United States, eastern Canada and the countries of western Europe. In later years, recruiting spread to the countries of eastern Europe. At different times in the CPR's settlement efforts, the company employed advertising and real estate agencies; sometimes, pressed for cash, they sold land outright to development companies. The declared aim of their advertising was to attract settlers, and they instructed their agents to discourage land speculators. Needless to say, when an agent was making a commission on every sale, his examination of the prospective client's motives for buying land in the Canadian West was often not as probing as it should have been.

The aims of the CPR were closely allied to those of the Dominion government in the matter of settling the west. There was no competition between them. Colonization meant that rail traffic would be developed, and so served the railway company's most important end. The rail companies sometimes entered into co-operative advertising ventures with the government. From 1908 to 1914, a Chicago agency was hired to conduct an extensive print advertising campaign. The Government of Canada, the CPR, the Grand Trunk Pacific and the Canadian Northern all paid equal shares of the retaining fee.

Advertisements selling the appeal of the Canadian West were placed in newspapers and magazines circulated to farming communities in the United States and Canada. Familiarization trips were organized by the agency. Editors and journalists were brought by rail to the area, free-of-charge, with the tacit understanding that they would subsequently write a piece for their journal on the attractions of the country in which they had been guests.

Choice Areas for Sale

The Famous Bow River Valley

Read what the *"Wanderer"* says about the Famous Bow River Valley in the rhyme below:

"Irrigation And Success."
A Rhyme by "The Canuck."
"The Song of the Wanderer."

I've wand'red in many foreign climes,
    Acrost the deep blue seas;
I've felt the bite of a wintry night,
    An' the breath o' the icy breeze;
I've stood on the burnin' tropic sands,
    My only home — a tent,
        An' I've kep' on wand'rin' an' wand'rin',
        Never — in no place — content.

But wander North or wander South, or wander East or West,
    Up in Baffin's Bay land, or Jerusalem the Blest,
If I didn't run on a C.P.R. Irrigatin' Ad on props,
    Statin' in great big letters, "Irrigatin' doubles crops."

It stared from the "Lunnon Cronikle,"
    It glared from the "Noo York World,"
It screamed from Chicago's "Tribune,"
    'Twas from the "Free Press" hurled;
An' pictur'd in the magazines,
    An' windows o' the shops,
        This ir-re-futable remark:
        "Irrigatin' doubles crops."

Then I drifted Calgar-y-wards,
    Hit the ties from the 'Peg to the Hat,
But there glared an' stared a big sign board,
    Like I seed in Samoa — on that
'Twas write in good, plain English,
    In letters as big as yer hand,
        "If ye wants bumper crops ye need water,
        "Irrigatin' 'll double yer land."

"Kismet! I cried in a whisper,
    I've come to the land o' my dreams —
Land that grows wheat — spring an' winter,
    Alfalfa, potatoes — would seem
To be plenty good fer a rover,
    A wand'rer, time worn an' spent;
        Here I settles, I farms, an' I marries,
        Ever — an' allus — content.

"Here's a climate supremely delightful,
    Th' government governin' right;
Irrigatin' pertects yer investment,
    No crops swep' away in a night,
Thirty bushel or more to the acre,
    Land cheap, an' on easy payment.
        Here I settles, I farms, an' I marries,
        Ever — an' allus — content.

"If I don't have the money — wot matter?
    I pays fer the land as I tills,
With instalments spread over long stretches,
    The crops, meantime, payin' the bills;
With advice from experienced farmers,
    From th' Company, don't cost a cent.
        Here I settles, I farms, an' I marries,
        Ever — an' allus — content."

The Canadian Pacific Irrigation Colonization Co.

Calgary   Alta.

A North Dakota land company which earlier had been remarkably effective in selling off dryland areas was chosen to act as agent for lands in the Western Section of the irrigation block. Dennis's dissatisfaction with their methods and results stimulated a reappraisal of the CPR's whole approach to settlement.

In 1912, a fundamental alteration in land policy occurred. All lands administration was centralized in the newly-created CPR Department of Natural Resources in Calgary and a policy of colonization, as opposed to land selling, was adopted and undertaken with zestful optimism. The aim was not just to get settlers onto the land but to keep them there.

The agency system was kept in place, with central agents located in strategic locales being responsible for a group of agents in the field. Once contact was made with a prospective settler, the agent forwarded his name to the Calgary office, which then went into action. A series of publications was sent out to the interested party over a period of months, so as to keep the idea of emigrating to Canada uppermost in his mind. Marketing of the irrigation block was pervasive and persistent; and, as some who succumbed to its lure would later charge, misleading to the point of falsehood. Friendly letters, written so as to appeal to the particular circumstances of the individual, accompanied the literature. If the prospective settler was located in an irrigation state, for instance, he received a completely different packet of materials from those mailed to someone unfamiliar with irrigation. The latter group was told that irrigation was easy and virtually foolproof, a claim to which an experienced irrigator would surely object. From 800,000 to 1,000,000 pieces of print material were distributed annually in the United States. In one year, 1913, the CPR Department of Natural Resources spent $11,000 to distribute this literature.

The primary target of the CPR recruiters was the farmer familiar with irrigation. Next, people with some kind of agricultural experience were sought. Those who had sufficient capital for a down payment, and enough extra to see them through the lag between arrival on their land and the first cash crop, were especially courted. When recruitment for the irrigation block was first launched, the CPR was confident it would have a headlong rush for its farms and would be in the advantageous position of being able to hand-pick the purchasers. Once again, as in the 1880's, this proved not to be the case, so further inducements were offered to speed up the settlement process. Loans for machinery, buildings and livestock were made available. For those with the wherewithal, the CPR's Development Branch could be contracted to do land work at a reasonable rate. By this means, the settler could arrange to have farm work started before he and his family actually made the move to their new home.

It was recognized that there would be a learning period in which new settlers could become acquainted with the techniques of water management. Irrigation is a skilled practice, and it was common knowledge that an irrigation farmer had to be made of better stuff than a dryland farmer. Any help the CPR could give to the new settler, it was reasoned, would spur him on to success. Demonstration farms were set up to accomplish this purpose and colonists were urged to make free use of the knowledge and information available from the staff there. Irrigation specialists were assigned to advise the farmers on which cultivation methods to employ with each crop, as well as how to irrigate for maximum yields.

Above: Gathering at Davies Ranch, Crawling Valley, 1909. The ranching way of life was radically altered when, in 1910, homestead lands were opened up *and* construction began on the irrigation project.

Below: Line-up of heavily-laden homesteaders' wagons at Hutton ferry, 35 miles NE of Bassano, Red Deer River, 1913.

The CPR was prepared to go further to ease the way of the settlers. The "ready-made farm" program was instituted. Under this scheme, a house and barn were built, a well dug and, in some cases, a portion of the land was levelled and sown to crop prior to the arrival of the settler. The cost of farm improvements was added on to the selling price of the land and amortized over the period of the farm mortgage.

Camp of CPR surveyors and engineers at ready-made farm, Gem area, 1913.

New farm home and barn, ready-made near Duchess, 1916. These buildings are still in use by descendants of original settlers.

Ready-made farms were put forth as an enticement for some of the groups targetted by the CPR for immigration to the irrigation block. In 1909, efforts were concentrated to bring farmers from Britain to a cluster of such farms in the Western Section. An extensive advertising campaign was undertaken which, it was thought, would be very appealing to land-scarce British farmers. The results proved to be disappointing. The campaign did, however, catch the attention of one influential individual, no less a personage than the Fourth Duke of Sutherland.

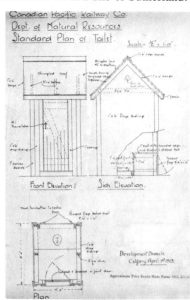

Standard plan for pre-fab toilet, CPR-DNR, Calgary, 1913. Cost — $25.

SUTHERLAND COLONY

The Fourth Duke of Sutherland was of an aristocratic lineage dating back to 1248, when the first Earl of Sutherland was created. When, in 1910, the Duke, a man of enormous wealth, alerted the CPR's Calgary office of his desire to purchase a large tract in the irrigation block of Alberta, there was not sufficient land left in the Western Section to accommodate his order. The profit to be made from such a big sale of land, along with the inestimable publicity of establishing such an impressive client in an irrigation area, outweighed the fact that the water delivery system in the Eastern Section was still under construction. Thus, it came about that the Duke bought 8,000 acres (3,240 ha) of land, east of Brooks, running north from the railway tracks. Today, the TransCanada Highway cuts through the original estate.

Cromartie Sutherland-Leveson-Gower, 4th Duke of Sutherland.

The Duke arranged with the CPR to oversee the preparation of several farms after the design of the company's ready-mades. These farms he planned to sell to deserving settlers. Prior to being accepted as land purchasers in the Duke's colony, prospects were interviewed and given the stamp of approval by his representatives. Advertisements were circulated in Great Britain for labourers and tradesmen to staff the remaining farmlands, which were retained by the Duke and operated under the direction of a manager.

In a very short time, the Sutherland Colony was a going concern. By 1914, nearly all the farmland was in crop. The cattle herd, begun in 1917, was built up and stabilized at between 3,000 and 4,000.

There was no stinting on the money spent to turn the Sutherland estate into an oasis on the prairie. Between 50 and 70 men were hired during the growing season. In addition to the cattle, several hundred Clydesdales and a string of saddle horses were kept until the day when mechanization made them redundant. Tree planting programs were carried out. The Duke of Sutherland himself is said to have brought Scotch pines, some of which survive to this day. With a large staff to level the land and tend to the crops, irrigation was benevolent. The soils were fertile and the crops flourished. It was the garden spot of the Eastern Section. Whenever CPR officials were "booming" the fruitfulness of irrigation to prospective settlers, they escorted them to the Sutherland Colony.

Certainly, water contributed to the bounty, but the Duke's bulging pocketbook was an advantage shared by very few other settlers. Jimmy Small, who was the farm manager from 1924 to 1928, recalled the turning point in the way in which work was done on the estate. The estate administrator from London had come to Brooks on an inspection tour and decided the time had come to change the farming operation over to mechanical power. He instructed Small to go to Brooks to order a tractor and plow. Obediently, the young manager jumped on his horse and was about to ride off when the administrator called him back and said, "Better order two . . . no, three . . . no, better order four outfits."

CPR officials advised their land agents in Great Britain that, in using the Duke's presence in Alberta as a drawing card to attract settlers, they were to stress that His Lordship was investing in the irrigation block only because he wanted to be a part of its glowing future. It does seem likely, however, that the change in the British tax law of 1908 which levied an onerous duty on inherited wealth was related to the Duke of Sutherland's heavy investment in Canadian properties two years later.

It was popularly believed that the Duke came to Alberta to make a personal selection of the lands he purchased. Whether this was the case, we do not know for sure; however, the visit of Their Graces, the Duke and Duchess of Sutherland, was closely noted and reported upon in *The Brooks Banner* of September 11, 1912:

> The Duke paid a visit to the demonstration farm and the irrigation headquarters Tuesday afternoon and was shown about the farm by the superintendent, Mr. Freng. The duke walked all over the farm and appeared to take the liveliest interest in all he saw. Wheat, barley, oats, corn and potatoes attracted his attention and he watched the process of harvesting the peas and spent some time examining the new metal granaries, four of which have been erected in the barley field. After leaving the farm in the automobile and visiting the irrigation headquarters the duke accompanied by his private secretary, walked back home, a distance of three miles. His grace, the Duke is quite a pedestrian, notwithstanding the fact that he uses a staff. In the morning he was out walking over his place at half past six.

FIRST STREET WEST, BROOKS, ALTA.

Early postcard view. Note wooden sidewalks.

The Duke had investments in other parts of Alberta — in Clyde and in Innisfail. As he seems to have been so interested in his farming operation here, it is possible the people of the new Brooks community might have enjoyed frequently the excitement of royal visits. Sadly, the Duke died the following year at Dunrobin Castle in Scotland. His heir, the Fifth Duke, was reputed to be something of a playboy. He showed no interest in Alberta, obviously preferring his yacht and the roll of the Mediterranean to the roll of the plains.

After the death of the Fourth Duke, the royal presence in Brooks was represented only by occasional visits from a London estate administrator. The Sutherland interests were overseen by a series of managers. Some of these took up residence in the "big house," the bungalow the Duke had built for himself and his wife in anticipation of frequent visits to his farm. The bungalow still stands, a charming reminder of our early brush with the aristocracy.

The Sutherland estate operated profitably for two decades but absentee landlordism eventually took its toll. The land was put up for sale in 1935, purchased by the EID and resettled.

A bulletin by the CPR used to recruit settlers featured the colony: *The Duke of Sutherland's Alberta Lands: Brooks and Clyde*, by R. B. Sangster. It is amusing to contrast the word picture it draws of Brooks with one left us by an ex-officer in the British army who worked on the Sutherland place as a horse skinner in 1925.

In Sangster's words:

> The people of Alberta and particularly in Brooks, are clever, bright, and most obliging. They are always ready to respond to an advance in so cheery a manner that the wheels of life cannot but run smoothly, and the newcomer meets everywhere with a real Jolly-Glad-You-Came-Here reception. Although there is a good sprinkling of Americans among them, the sentiment is Anglo-Canadian of the best kind. The law is fully respected and drunkenness must be rare as I never saw a case.

The unbuttoned prose of a man writing to his family back home presents a somewhat different appraisal:

> The town of Brooks would amuse you awfully. I went in with the rest on Saturday night, as we always do, to buy supplies of tobacco and reading materials for the coming week, and it was just like a frontier town on the pictures. Rows of ponies standing asleep, each one under a huge saddle; rows of wagons all harnessed up also with their horses fast asleep — and then the difference between the real and the movie. Fords innumerable, they too fast asleep, if Fords do sleep. Cowboys, semi-cowboys, farm hands, horse-skinners like myself, C.P.R. railroad workers (mostly Irish), and C.P.R. irrigation workers — the engineers all Americans and the labourers Finns and Swedes.
>
> The eating houses are all Chinese or Japanese, and so are the laundries, but all the other shops are Canadian. The only brick building is the hotel, and that's got a wooden shingle roof. The town is very proud of itself because it has got pavements — I beg their pardon, sidewalks — but they are made like big duck boards, and if you step on the edge of the sidewalk, one of the slats is liable to rise up and hit you on the side of the head. There is a station but no platform or ticket office and passenger trains only stop there by signal.
>
> The men came back from town the other Saturday in a terrible state — been fighting with irrigators from the CPR and had apparently won. Teamsters in this country have a terrible reputation, and their favourite weapon is a single-tree off a wagon-pole which is very heavy and has an iron end with a curly hook where the trace is fastened to. Anyway the wagon came back with both single-trees broken and everyone cut and bruised. They say it was a nice fight till one of the CPR [men] raised his spade, and after that it got a bit rough, and the mountie came and sent them all home.

SETTLEMENT GOES FORWARD

World War I broke out in 1914. It was a determining factor in the course of settlement in the Eastern Section. Colonists who might have been attracted from Britain, Europe and eastern Canada were mired down in the trenches of the battlefields. Since the United States was not actively involved in the war until 1917, all of the CPR's settlement efforts were beamed south of the border.

Back when irrigation on the prairie was still under consideration, the Canadian government assigned Pearce and Dennis to come up with a proposal as to how best to proceed with settlement in an irrigation block. Their report advocated the use of a hamlet, or colony, system. Under this plan, the settlers would build their homes and outbuildings in a central spot, from where they would go out to their farms on adjacent lands. Although this rather medieval plan was never attempted, Dennis adhered to the ideal of establishing families of like religious or ethnic backgrounds in close proximity to one another — the reasoning behind this being that the settlers would be less subject to loneliness in the raw new land if their neighbours were from the same background. It was rationalized that they would be more likely to stick out the first trying years if they had friends with whom to commiserate.

The first group of settlers brought to the Eastern Section by the CPR under this plan came to a ready-made farm colony near Gem, known for some years after that as the Bassano Colony. Most of them were experienced irrigationists from Colorado. They arrived in the spring of 1914.

Why would farmers leave one irrigation area to come to another? The price of the land was the lure. Land values in the irrigation block fluctuated somewhat according to the market but, on average, an acre of irrigable land sold for $50, compared with prices in the $300-per-acre range for similar land in the irrigated areas of the United States.

This first group of colonists was very special to the district. A CPR land agent shepherded them the entire way from Colorado to Bassano. Upon arrival,

Colorado settlers (bound for ready-made irrigation colony at Gem) arrive by special train. Bassano, March 1914.

they were met at the station by the Mayor and served a banquet, prior to being escorted by team and democrat to view the damsite. Following a tour of the dam, they were again offered refreshment, this time in the form of tea served under the dam.

There is no record of the welcome accorded the next group brought to the area. Certainly, great efforts were extended by the CPR to get them here. These people were renters and labourers on sugar beet farms in Nebraska. Although the promise of land ownership would seem an adequate enticement for such a group, it took some time for the CPR to persuade them to relocate. One of the reasons for their reluctance was that many of them were extremely poor. Even had the down payment for a farm been within their reach, they could not afford the cost of the move nor the machinery to start farming. Group loyalty seems to have been strong among them; they would come as a group or not at all.

Because they were hard-working and experienced in the art of irrigation, these people were deemed highly desirable as colonists. Finally, when the CPR offered to extend loans for machinery and horses, credit the cost of transportation, and grant a three-year period of grace between the time of the down payment and the next installment on their farms, they moved to the West Duchess area in 1916. Although they were referred to as the Russian Colony by the CPR, they were of German origin and German was their language.

It was reasonable to suppose that the new settlers to the irrigation sections would be so enthused with their surroundings that they would communicate their feelings to friends and family back home. From this, more settlement would

Gem P.O., Alberta,
November 14th, 1914.

I came to Southern Alberta about a year ago from Colorado, and can see no great difference in climatic conditions here and in Eastern Colorado.

We can raise everything here that can be raised in Colorado except melons, while potatoes, small grains and alfalfa yield far better here than in Colorado.

The soil, which is a chocolate loam, is very

L. B. McBRIDE'S HOUSE—Bassano Colony.

productive under irrigation, and there is no doubt that the C.P.R. have the best irrigation system in the world.

It was clearly demonstrated here this year that with irrigation, crops could be forced during the growing season and thereby eliminate all danger from frost, and from a mixed farming standpoint, I consider the Bassano colony second to none. Plowing was in full blast until November 13th, when a light snow stopped us.

(Sgd.) D. C. FORTNEY.

"Personal Experiences" of Gem's first settlers.

Gem P.O., Alberta,
November 12th, 1914.

Having arrived in Canada on March 10th, and going on a raw piece of land without a furrow broken, we will say this in regard to our first year's farming.

We started to break prairie about April 10th. We planted 40 acres of barley, and 30

L. B. McBRIDE'S BARN—Bassano Colony.

acres of oats, about May 25th, but it was so dry that the grain would not sprout until it was irrigated about June 20th. With only one irrigation the barley made 16 bushels per acre, and the oats made 30 bushels per acre. Had we irrigated it again, there is no question but it would have made double the yield. This grain was all well matured and oats weighed 40 lbs. per bushel, and the barley is above standard weight. Had we not been persuaded that another irrigation would prevent the ripening of the grain, we would have irrigated more.

If you get your crops up in proper time in the spring, there is no question but that they will mature. A man with a limited capital, but willing to work, will make good here.

(Sgd.) C. W. JONES.
H. P. FERGUSON.

ensue. The CPR took this supposition a step further, and institutionalized it. They formed "Extension of Settlement Clubs" and prepared brochures for each little community that became involved with the company in promoting its area. The members of the clubs furnished the Calgary office with the names and addresses of anyone they could think of who might be interested in emigrating to join them in their colony.

One of these pamphlets was produced for the Gem settlers shortly after their arrival. It was entitled "Bassano Irrigation Colony Extension of Settlement Club." Several pages are devoted to describing the area: its climate, facilities, the irrigation system, the administration of water rights, improved farm plans, the crops, etc. It is glowingly optimistic about the future, telling its readers that "It will not not be long before we are recognized as the banner alfalfa district of Canada" and "Being able to produce these forage and grain crops with ease and in vast quantities, undoubtedly we are to develop into one of the greatest cattle finishing districts on the continent." Photographs of waist-high barley fields and a sturgeon-sized fish said to have been hooked below Bassano Dam accompany the text. A section entitled "Personal Experiences" is perhaps the most telling in the booklet. It prints letters written by the settlers themselves relating their experiences in their new homes and urging others to join them.

It was expected that colonies anchored upon religious affiliations would have the necessary stabilizing strength to survive. Working through settlement boards within particular denominations, the CPR contacted potential immigrants with the proposal that they select a delegate from among their number to come and examine lands in the irrigation block which could then be reserved exclusively for them. If the prospect was appealing to the delegate, he would promote the move to his friends and neighbours. The colonists were encouraged to bring a pastor with them so that their community might be centered upon the church.

St. John the Baptist Roman Catholic Church, as it looked in 1948. Built in 1917 by French-Canadian settlers at Rosemary Colony (Clemenceau).

J. L. Carroll Photographics Ltd.

Sometimes this worked, sometimes it failed. A group of Roman Catholic French Canadians settled around their church west of Rosemary. It remained a landmark for years after its builders had left for other parts. There are also examples in the District that bear testimony to satisfactory results from the pursuit of this policy. The Swedish Lutheran colony in Scandia was settled in 1918 and the Danish Lutherans came to the Tilley area in 1929. Mennonites from Pennsylvania settled early and have stayed on in the Duchess area. The descendants of these pioneers are still a part of the District today. Their names are borne now by the fourth generation to live here.

With all the able-bodied men on the battlefields of Europe, a shortage of farm labour in the West was a by-product of the first world war. Harvest excursion trains from other parts of Canada were operated by the CPR to overcome this difficulty. The underlying hope was that the excursionists would decide not to return to wherever they came from but would stay to settle in the West. To this end, whole families were transported free-of-charge to various points on the prairies.

In spite of the tremendous expense and effort put forth by Dennis and his co-workers, settlement of the Eastern Section proved to be slower and more difficult than it had been for the Western Section. Dry lands were still available in Alberta and much less expensive than the irrigated ones. Farming dry was also easier than irrigating. Rumours of the disagreements between farmers on the Western Section and the CPR may have had some influence, too. Certainly, the Great War was a severely restricting factor.

The declaration of peace was expected to bring an injection of badly-needed settlers to the project. In anticipation of this, the CPR prepared 50 ready-made farms in the Tilley area designated for veterans. This cluster of farms was named the St. Julien Colony, after one of the battle-fields of the Great War. Lands to be subsidized for returning soldiers had to be agreed upon by the Canadian government. Alkali conditions, resulting from seepage, had arisen on some of the irrigated land in the Eastern Section. Fearing that it would present a problem in the Tilley area, the Soldiers' Settlement Board, a federal agency charged to assist returning military men to settle on farms, ruled the St. Julien Colony unsuitable for its intended purpose.

The CPR was, understandably, reluctant to accept the condemnation of such a large part of the Tilley area. In the year 1917, a contract was made with Asael Palmer, a young soils specialist whose name was to become famous in agricultural circles. He was to carry out extensive tests in the area to determine whether, in fact, the Canadian government chemists had judged the soil correctly. Palmer concluded that they had not. Sixty years of irrigation on the farms of the area have substantiated his judgement.

CPR staff continued to crop and irrigate most of the St. Julien farms until, in the early 1920's, settlers who had homesteaded at Alderson, to the east of the project, began to move onto them. What little money these farmers may have had to start with had sizzled away — like the crops they tried to grow on dry land. They entered into rental or share-cropping agreements with the CPR in the hope of eventually getting ahead enough to buy land once more.

Most of the movement to irrigated farms in the early 1920's was the result of drylanders shifting from their homestead lands. From the east, they migrated to Tilley; from the Lomond/Vauxhall area, they moved to the Bow Slope; and from north of the Red Deer River, they came to the Patricia and Millicent areas.

Between the years 1922 and 1929, the CPR and its subsidiary, the Canada Colonization Association, collaborated with the Mennonite Land Settlement Board and the government Department of Immigration and Colonization to organize the emigration of over 10,000 Mennonites from Russia, where they had been existing in very distressed circumstances. They were settled in various parts of Canada, but the portion of the group destined for the irrigation block began to arrive in the mild and open winter of 1928-29. By spring, 36 families had taken their places in the Gem, Rosemary and Countess areas.

Sketch of the Mennonite church built in Rosemary, 1940. Earlier services were held in converted CPR barn. Several EID communities now have Mennonite congregations. Artist: Sharon Dyck.

A special dispensation of a ban on Mennonite immigration was given by the government to make possible this large-scale movement. Attitudes to immigration were changing. Prior to this time, the bias in recruitment policy was toward British and western European settlers. Clifford Sifton, who was Minister of the Interior from 1896 to 1905, thought that, ". . . a stalwart peasant in a sheepskin coat, born of the soil, whose forefathers have been farmers for ten generations, with a stout wife and half a dozen children . . ." was the ideal settler. However, the peoples of eastern Europe were not courted until it became obvious that the great western spaces were *not* going to be filled by eager Anglo-Saxons. Asians were simply not considered. This shift in the emphasis of immigration brought a sweeping wave of settlement to Canada. The late 1920's and early 1930's saw the arrival of Hungarians, Czechoslovakians, Lithuanians, Ukrainians and Poles in the Eastern Section.

There is no evidence that the CPR or the Dominion Government conducted the kinds of market surveys, so popular in our day, to gauge the response of the consumers of settlement propaganda. Therefore, it remains unknown which of the many methods of attracting settlers was most effective. The largest number of immigrants to the Eastern Section, however, came from the country where the greatest amounts of money and effort had been expended — the United States.

Individual decisions to come to the area were made as a result of wide-spread advertising. The Czechoslovakian community in Tilley grew from a small nucleus of settlers who were lured to the irrigation block by advertisements in a Slovak newspaper, published in the United States and circulated both there and in Canada. Some of these men were already in this country, working in the coal mines of the Crowsnest Pass; others had come as labourers to the Pennyslvania mines.

The cell of settlement grew. Local agents were employed by the CPR to solicit testimonial letters from the settlers, directed to their fellow nationals in Czechoslovakia. In most cases, wives and families had been left behind in the "old country" and personal communications passing to and fro across the Atlantic spread the word. To paraphrase a current television commercial, "I told two friends and then they told two friends, and so on, and so on, and so on . . ."

THE TROUBLES BEGIN

Settlement progress was discouraging for the CPR during the years of World War I but it picked up following the armistice; 1919 was a high point when land sales over the previous year practically doubled. Farm prices were good and the future looked promising. But optimistic hopes that colonization in the Eastern Section had reached the beginning of an upward trend were soon dampened. Immigration continued and efforts to settle people on the land were as vigorous as always, but the first hints surfaced of severe problems to follow. Between the spring and fall of 1920 came the first sharp decline in the prices offered for both livestock and grain. The next year brought more of the same.

The agricultural depression preceded the more general depression of the 1930's by almost a decade. The situation facing farmers, generally, was that while the prices of goods and services they had to buy remained disproportionately high, returns for the commodities they produced were very low. This was an unhappy state of affairs for farmers everywhere. In the Eastern Section of the irrigation block, the problems were compounded by the fact that, for most settlers, there had been no period in which to get established before the hard times struck. Anyone who has relocated understands that a time of adjustment to new surroundings can be difficult — even without pressing financial worries. Newcomers to the area were faced, not only with the drastic social upheaval of arrival in a new land with few amenities, but with a downward spiral in agricultural prices which slashed their livelihood to bare subsistence. By 1931, it cost more to produce a bushel of wheat than it was worth.

The decade of the 1920's had hardly begun when a period of transience set in. Original settlers packed their belongings, sure the CPR had sold them a pack of goods. New people arrived to try their luck in Sunny Alberta; and often, they too threw up their hands in defeat. A few lucky ones were able to sell or rent their farms. Most simply abandoned them. Some of the people who stayed say that the comings and goings were so commonplace as to be unworthy of remark. During the fall, one farm auction followed on the heels of another. The story is told of a family who arrived in the Patricia area in the fall, hunkered down for the winter and left with the arrival of the meadowlarks in the spring. It was remarked, ruefully, that they were probably smarter than most.

Concern for the farmers' plight was expressed by Gus Griffin, the CPR Superintendent for Operation and Maintenance in Brooks, in his annual report for 1923. He speaks of the exodus of farmers and the "morale of the settlers at low ebb." Very sensibly, he argues that it costs money to put a settler on the land and that it is in the company's interest to hang onto them. Land sales were made from the CPR Department of Natural Resources in Calgary and any dealings with regard to adjustments to land contracts, problems with payments — in fact, anything to do with the business end of land contracts — had to take place there. This was an irritation that grated on the farmers, who could ill afford trips to Calgary to deal with the Lands people. When a farmer did put forth the money to go to the Calgary office, he was faced with a battery of officials, each with responsibility for a narrow chunk of the action. Often, the poor farmer was unable to sort out the pecking order and departed with the frustrated feeling of having bungled through a bureaucratic maze to no good end.

Glenbow Archives.

CPR Irrigation and Colonization Building, 9 Ave. and 1 St. S.W., Calgary.

Griffin advises, "It is my earnest opinion that the Company can with advantage to the settlers and to itself and at no additional cost modify its organization for dealing with settlers on the Eastern Section by locating a representative with responsibility and authority at Brooks." This person "would be much better informed . . . and come in contact with the settlers more often and more naturally and would understand them and their business much more accurately and intimately."

Hindsight is not a particularly valuable sense but it is interesting to muse on how things might have gone had Griffin's superiors hearkened to his advice. Unfortunately, the situation remained unchanged and frictions built up between the farmers and the CPR. In 1928, Don Bark, who was director of the Irrigation Investigation Branch, had his duties expanded to take care of collections of land payments and water rentals in Brooks, but it was still necessary for water users to make the trip to Calgary to effect any adjustment to their contracts.

Most farms were made up of a combination of irrigable and non-irrigable land. Irrigable land sold for between $25 and $50 per acre; non-irrigable land, which was rough or at a higher elevation than the delivery point of water to the farm, was lower priced. These prices were considered very reasonable when compared with what was being asked for similar land in the irrigated areas of the United States, where the price per acre was between $200 and $300. The terms of the purchase agreements between the farmer and the CPR differed in their particulars but, in general, the down payment was one-twentieth of the purchase price, the remainder to be paid in equal installments over a 20-year period. Interest was set at six percent. If the farmer required a loan to finance machinery or livestock, it was granted him and added to the purchase price when computing the mortgage payments. If a ready-made farm was bought, the cost of the farm improvements was also added to the purchase price. Some contracts were based on crop-sharing agreements. Over and above the price of the land, water rentals were set at $1.25 per acre annually.

There was nothing devious about the contracts; they were simple straightforward mortgages. Where the trouble arose was with the terribly depressed prices for farm products. Put another way, the farmers found themselves in much the same situation as those who over-extended themselves prior to our most recent recession in the 1980's. They simply could not make enough from their farms to meet contract payments. Different from farmers and businessmen of recent years, however, they rarely experienced the pain of having their property repossessed. Quite the opposite was the case. Because the CPR desired to keep settlers on the land at all costs, they were allowed to get further and further in arrears on both their land contracts and water rental agreements. This bad situation was made much worse by the ugly fact of interest charges. With a six percent surcharge on the unpaid principal each year, plus interest on all back payments for land and water rentals, there were many farmers who, after they had been working them for ten years, owed more for their farms than the original purchase price.

There had been problems on the Western Section of the irrigation block for years. These had arisen over the classification of land, with landowners declaring they had paid irrigation prices for land that was not irrigable. These complaints led to an extensive reclassification of land by the Department of the Interior and the CPR in the years from 1911 to 1914. Water rates created trouble, too. Many years were wet enough to grow excellent grain crops in the Western Section, without irrigation. The farmers objected strenuously to having to pay for irrigation water they were not using. The CPR reasoned that, to maintain and operate an irrigation system, water rentals had to be collected on a yearly basis. Some very unhappy farmers argued that the frost-free season in the area was too short for irrigation to be of any benefit at all, and that all the land should be sold at the lower price of non-irrigable land.

Problems surfaced later in the Eastern Section. Unlike the farmers in the Western Section, those in the Eastern Section agreed that irrigation was necessary. Although their water rates were much higher than those paid in the Western Section, they were not seen as extortionary. Land classification, however, was a contentious issue. Originally, the land had been classified by engineers from the Department of the Interior under the same guidelines as those used in the Western Section. After several years of irrigation, alkali problems manifested themselves and contract holders objected to paying for such unproductive land.

Laden with debt, the contract holders found many aspects of the CPR's policy abrasive. The meeting minutes of the Scandia UFA repetitiously record the dispatch of letters and petitions to the CPR asking that a railway be built to the Bow Slope. The company had promised, when the first settlers came in 1918, that a spur line would shortly be constructed to connect their area with the main line. There is no understanding the CPR's reluctance to carry out this obligation. It was not until 1928 that the company made good its promise, much too late to avert the antagonism that had rankled for a decade. Although the Bow Slope and Gem were among the first communities to be settled, they were the last to be linked by rail to market centres.

Dragging of the heels is, no doubt, inherent in the nature of bureaucracies, but such delays seemed unnecessary aggravations to the farmers. An interchange among the Department of the Interior, the CPR and a farmer from Cassils serves to illustrate the sorts of irritations that, left untreated, could fester and swell into hatred of the CPR.

Seepage from the main canal running through Fred Bechdholt's farm caused an alkali problem. He reported this in person to the office of the Commissioner of Irrigation at the Department of the Interior in Calgary on June 4th, 1926. Presumably, he had previously taken the matter up with the CPR Department of Natural Resources, as his complaint dated back to 1922. Bechdholt's stated conviction was that the CPR should construct the necessary drains to prevent extension of the salt problems and he asked the federal government, through the Department of the Interior, to reclassify the land affected. In the way of government, the official who heard Bechdholt's grievance asked for it in writing.

Legally, the CPR was not liable for the damage done by canal seepage, but in the interests of keeping Bechdholt in the district, some unnamed company official had offered to allow him another farm in exchange for the damaged one. The farmer had expended a good deal of money on buildings and fences but the same company official gave it as his opinion that financial compensation would not be forthcoming from the company, should Bechdholt wish to move any of these structures to the other farm.

Bechdholt refused the offer. He also refused to make payments on his contract until the damage to his farm was rectified. At the time of his appeal to the commissioner of irrigation, he had withheld payments for four years. Bechdholt delayed sending his complaint in writing as he had been requested to do. The reason for this delay was given in a letter to the commissioner of irrigation of September 25, 1926, in which he says that the CPR had given him assurance that his problems would be investigated. Now, the fall had come round and still nothing had been done by the CPR. To add insult to injury, Bechdholt says, "I have been told by a neighbour that a CPR official has made the statement that they are going to kick me off the land this fall." Bechdholt's experience was not untypical.

Squabbles with the CPR did not consume the energies of all of the farmers all of the time. There were innumerable things to be accomplished in addition to the demanding labours of farming. Post offices, roads, schools and medical services were all lacking and the builders of new communities worked persistently to secure better facilities.

Schools were a priority and they were established rather quickly following settlement. By 1922, 21 schools were listed in the annual report of the CPR Operation and Maintenance Division.

A letter of October 8, 1920 written by the commissioner of irrigation, F. H. Peters, to a superior in the Department of the Interior in Ottawa speaks of the deplorable condition of the roads.

> One thing that is very noticeably lacking in this district [the CPR Eastern Section] is the construction of roads. The country is very flat, and a great many of the shallow depressions running through the land have been filled with waste water, so that it is very difficult to drive from Millicent to Countess in a motor car.

As Peters was on an inspection tour of the Eastern Section, impassable roads were, no doubt, a considerable hindrance. How much more obstructive they were for those who had to travel them to deliver grain to an elevator 20 miles distant, or to rush a sick child to the hospital in Bassano or Medicine Hat! Depending upon the starting point, a trip to Bow City for coal could be a two or three-day undertaking.

Bill Sheldrake.

Inadequate drainage caused problems on main Duchess-Millicent road, 1930's.

THE UNITED FARMERS OF ALBERTA

The United Farmers of Alberta organized in 1909 to address the concerns of the rural population of the province. For more than a decade, the co-operative lobbied with governments of the day for more group action to solve some of the problems confronting them.

The actions the UFA deemed appropriate were not forthcoming. Finally, out of exasperation, the organization became politicized. The Progressive Party was formed and candidates nominated; in the election of 1921, the farmers' party decisively unseated the Liberals.

At the beginning of the 1920's, local chapters of the United Farmers of Alberta were formed around the project. Soon the Local became the gathering place at which various matters of concern to the community were tackled. One of the functions of the Locals was to purchase supplies, such as binder twine, seed and lumber, in quantity. The duty of dispensing these goods among the members fell to the secretary-treasurer who was paid a small commission for his services.

Road work was also undertaken through the UFA Locals. A road boss was elected who was responsible to determine which of all the bad roads was to be given priority on the repair list. He then took the money allotted for roads in his district and contracted for the work to be done by his fellow community members. The few dollars earned for this work was often a welcome supplement to a meagre farm income.

Life was not all hard work. Socializing was an important pillar of moral support for the struggling communities. Church and school were central to life. Picnics, concerts, fairs, always-popular amateur theatricals, and the occasional hosting of the Chautauqua were organized through the local UFA and the women's arm of the movement, the UFWA. In essence, this was the governing body of the community, so it is not surprising that it was through the UFA Locals that the farmers rallied to protest their sorry economic position.

The CPR was not oblivious to the difficult straits of the farmer. When wheat prices fell in 1920 and continued to drop, a petition was signed by 272 contract holders in the Eastern Section, asking for a two-year moratorium on their payments to allow them to put any capital they could amass toward buying livestock. The CPR acquiesced. Unfortunately, conditions were such that the cessation of payments made little difference to the farmers' lot. Product prices continued to fall and, once taxes and water rates were paid, there was not enough money left after harvest to meet the basic needs of the family — let alone get started in livestock.

In May of 1923, E. W. Beatty, President of the CPR, announced that contracts with land purchasers in the West were to be amortized over a 34-year period in an attempt to ease the obligations under which farmers laboured. The two-year moratorium was still in effect in the Eastern Section where Beatty's well-publicized announcement caused concern and consternation. Reassurance was given by local CPR employees that the Eastern Section was exempt for the period agreed upon earlier. Then in 1924, when the moratorium was up, the farmers would be offered — but not forced to accept — 34-year agreements. This announcement went some way to allay fears; however, resentments against the CPR were never far beneath the surface and might erupt at any provocation.

One of the severest critics of the CPR was a man called W. D. Trego, who farmed on rented land in the Gleichen district of the Western Section. He had come with his wife and family in 1906 from Idaho. At the International Irrigation Congress held in Calgary in 1914, Trego challenged several of the speakers. Finally, when he prolonged an argument by taking the stance that it was impossible to over-winter alfalfa in Alberta, the chairman rebuked him mildly, suggesting that his grievances were personal and did not apply to the area as a whole.

Mr. A. L. Fryberger, who had come to the Gem colony the previous year, was also at the meeting. He told the assembled group that Mr. Trego had met the trainload of settlers from Colorado when they arrived at Bassano and advised them that the use of water would retard the growth of their crops. As a result, according to Fryberger, the colonists did not use water in the way they had learned in Colorado, with the consequence that their crops suffered badly in the very dry summer of 1914.

Trego seems to have been a born agitator. According to an account given by his son in the local history, *The Gleichen Call*, he certainly prospered in Alberta. Although he bought a farm in Arrowwood in 1917, he continued to rent the Gleichen farm, that same farm on which he had contended alfalfa could not be grown. In addition, he leased land in the Wintering Hills on which he ran "a large number of cattle."

In 1923, Trego sent a circular letter to all UFA locals in the CPR irrigation project soliciting their support for a scheme of the Contract Holders' Association to force concessions from the CPR. The bottom line was that unless the CPR met the farmers' demands by a certain day, they would tack "For Sale" signs on their gate posts and depart to take up lands in Bolivia.

Early in 1924, Trego came to the Eastern Section to seek support. The Bow Slope locals, according to a *Brooks Bulletin* report, were solidly behind Trego but he met with little enthusiasm elsewhere in the district.

Support was also lacking among his fellow Western Section farmers. An open letter, published in *The Calgary Herald* by a number of those in disagreement with Trego, deplored his bullying techniques and pointed out that conditions were no worse there than they were for farmers everywhere.

Impetus for the Trego plan seems to have petered out: at any rate, no exodus of poor persecuted farmers to far away South America took place.

In response to the problems encountered on the Eastern Section, with regard to alkali or otherwise uncultivable land, the CPR began a program of land reclassification in 1924. In the summer of that year, 414 contract holders were interviewed about their situations. Of these, 186 registered complaints about their lands. Almost 7,000 acres (2,850 ha) were affected.

Colonel Doughty, the Assistant General Superintendent of Lands, was stationed in Brooks to carry out the reclassification program. This was not quickly accomplished, as each complaint was carefully studied and, before reclassifying the land, an attempt was made to determine whether the farmer, in co-operation with the company, might reclaim the affected lands. Purchase payments and water rates on bad areas were stopped until the land was once again productive. When the project began in 1914, 440,000 acres (178,200 ha) were assessed to be irrigable. Following reclassification, the number of irrigable acres dropped to 250,000 (101,250 ha). Here it remained until the recent introduction of sprinkler irrigation moved estimates of potentially irrigable acreage upward again.

As the decade wore on, the situation in the Eastern Section became more and more critical. The farmers who stayed on, trying from year to year to improve their farms, hoping against hope that markets would take an upswing, were in some ways worse off than those who had decided early on to take their losses and run. The more time and effort the farmer put into his place, the harder it was for him to leave it. The CPR made no concessions for improvements that had been made at the farmer's expense.

Don Bark, head of the CPR Irrigation Investigation Branch in Brooks, summed up the behaviour that could erupt when frustrations mounted: "One is wont to kick the dog, abuse the wife or best friend or cuss the CPR."

Certainly, there was plenty of the latter. It is not difficult to imagine the resentment resulting from falling ever further into debt and knowing your tenure on the land was by the good grace of a corporation that seemed impersonal and unconcerned. Trust diminished and anxiety grew.

Close to home, the cleft between CPR employees and the local farmers widened. A farmer, left with only five dollars in his pocket after the year's bills had been paid, every last kernel of grain was at the elevator and every calf had been shipped, was bound to look with anger at the chauffeur-driven wife of one of the engineers on her way to the train station. There, using her free pass, she would board the train to spend the day shopping in Calgary.

The houses of the EID employees in Evergreen Park seem modest enough by modern standards but, in 1930, when most of the farming community and the local

Part of "the Row" of CPR houses.

people were being pulverized by grinding poverty, "Rotten Row," as it was called, seemed to flaunt itself in the face of destitution.

Concessions were again offered to the contract holders in 1927 and 1928. But they were of no real significance. Nothing but a complete obliteration of accumulated debts and a repricing of the land held on contract would have made any substantial difference.

The CPR's reluctance to take this step was presumably based upon its responsibility to its stockholders. The amount of capital invested in the structures of the irrigation system necessitated attempts to recoup these expenditures through land sales. It was a futile undertaking. More time and money went down the drain in bookkeeping, collections, settling and re-settling the land than was justified by the amounts realized from sales.

Several proposals to reprice the land according to its ability to produce income were put forward by the contract holders to the CPR — but to no avail. This was definitely not a radical notion, nor was it novel. The experience of other irrigation projects in North America showed that setting a high price on irrigated land, based upon its presumed ability to produce higher yields, is impractical. When the increased costs of labour and machinery required for irrigation farming are subtracted from the high gross profits, the net profit margin is not enough to justify greater land costs. Published in 1924, a report on the investigation of problematic irrigation projects by the United States Reclamation Service addressed, among other problems, the pricing of land,

> . . . the present method of repayment of project construction costs, based upon time and percentages of cost, instead of the ability of the several classes of lands to produce, is unscientific and difficult of fulfillment . . . annual acre repayment charge should be 5 percent of the productive power of the lands.

Alberta had become a province in 1905, but it was not until 1930 that control of natural resources, including water, was turned over by the federal government to the province. For all intents and purposes, then, matters pertaining to irrigation had been affected very little by Alberta's birth. The irrigation commissioner of the federal Department of the Interior was still responsible to ensure that private corporations met the conditions of their irrigation licenses. Arbitration between aggrieved farmers and the CPR came under the wing of the irrigation commissioner and classification of lands required the approval of his department.

After 1930, the Government of Alberta created the Irrigation Council, and all matters pertaining to irrigation in the province then came under the jurisdiction of this body.

Through the years, farmers of the Eastern Section had directed petitions to the government for assistance. After 1930, petitions and resolutions continued to be drafted. The only change was that this barrage of paper was directed at MLA's in Alberta's UFA government, rather than to the federal ministers.

It is well to introduce at this point two individuals who played dominant roles in their respective UFA locals and were to strongly influence events leading to the creation of the EID. Both men are still living in the District at the time of writing and have helped to outline the sequence of happenings and give some of the flavour of the times.

Bill Sheldrake.   Carl Anderson.

Bill Sheldrake was born in London, England in 1894. He came to the Duchess area in 1916 with other members of his family, after a stint at homesteading in Saskatchewan. Sheldrake was active in the Duchess UFA from its inception. When the District UFA was formed in 1928, he served as secretary-treasurer for some years. Besides working for the improvement of conditions in his area, Sheldrake was an active organizer in the politicizing of the UFA. In recognition of his work, he was invited to stand for election in the farmers' government. He declined, but continued to work hard in the back rooms.

Elected president of the District UFA at its formation, Carl Anderson is so well known in the area that he hardly needs an introduction. He was the general manager of the EID from 1947 to 1964 and served as a trustee on the board for years prior to that. As a young man, Anderson came from Nebraska, where he was born, to the Scandia area. Settlement in Scandia was exclusively Swedish until after 1921 and a tightly-knit community resulted. From its formation in 1920, the Scandia UFA was well-attended and progressive in its approach to problems confronting the farmers.

The District UFA grew out of the perception on the part of the farmers that numbers would equal strength. While the UFA Locals, working independently, had not been successful in bringing the CPR to a serious bargaining position, it was thought that if they banded together, they might be able to overcome the company's resistance. In order to further augment their position, the District association decided to join the Contract Holders' Association, which had been in existence in the Western Section for years. At the beginning of January 1931, the Eastern Section branch of the Contract Holders Association was formed at a meeting in Duchess. Soon, farmers from other parts of the district joined the group.

Grassroots UFA support was essential to the UFA government in Edmonton. As a result, very soon after assuming control of the province's natural resources, the government set up a Board of Enquiry to survey the conditions affecting CPR contract holders.

O. S. Longman, who at the time was director of the Olds School of Agriculture, and was later made Deputy Minister of Agriculture, was the committee member who investigated complaints in the field. He interviewed about 100 farmers in the Eastern and Western Sections.

Longman forecast the trend of the future when he suggested that income for the individual farmer could be increased by communal use of the extensive grasslands in the Eastern Section. He acknowledged that the change to a livestock economy could not be achieved overnight and that the ability of the contract holders to make their payments had to be assessed on their current incomes.

The final conclusions of his part of the report were almost precisely in line with what farmers' organizations had been claiming for many years. Income from the land was too low to make adherence to the terms of the CPR contracts a possibility. Longman accepted the declaration that the CPR had misled the settlers in selling them land at prices such that it had been impossible, even for the very best of farmers, to meet their payments. He urged that "the purchasers have a very strong moral claim for an equitable re-adjustment of their liabilities."

As a result of this report, which had been supplemented by persistent petitions from members of the Contract Holders' Association to their Members of the Legislative Assembly, representatives from both Sections of the irrigation project were invited, along with CPR personnel, to appear before the Legislative Assembly's Agriculture Committee. The date was March 19, 1931. Elected to tell the Eastern Section's story were: Bill Sheldrake, a man from Imperial Colony named "Red" (probably Bill Justin), and a third man whose name is now forgotten.

Speaking for the CPR was George A. Walker, chief legal counsel for its Department of Natural Resources. As we shall see, Walker was to be a key figure in events leading to the creation of the Eastern Irrigation District. At this hearing, Walker took the position that the CPR was not to blame for economic conditions affecting the agricultural industry everywhere. The company, he said, had made concessions to the farmers in the irrigation project in the past and was prepared to do what it could to help their situation in future. He stated that, from 1929 to 1931, the company had paid $700,000 in tax arrears for settlers on CPR lands, in order to save their farms from forfeiture.

Interest charges were the most offensive aspect of the contracts. Early in 1932, the CPR announced that all interest charges from the previous year would be written off unconditionally. Other concessions involving share-cropping were made, in which the company would accept one-third share of the crop, whatever its market value, in lieu of one yearly installment of principal and interest. In 1933 and again in 1934, there was a further easing of contract stipulations. Water rental was to be written off and only one-quarter share of the crop was required to meet a yearly payment on the land.

All of these complicated schemes to relieve the farmers' hardships were commendable but the economic times were so out of joint that a farm family could hope for little more than survival. There was no way that taxes, water rentals and land payments could all be made from farm income. This was a time when sale of the best crops ever raised by a farmer could leave him in debt. In 1933, the worth of the wheat produced in all of Canada was less than the value of what had been grown in 1928 by Alberta alone.

Throughout 1933, the District UFA struggled to come up with a solution that would be both acceptable to the CPR and of some real benefit to the farmers. The executive committee met frequently with CPR officials in Calgary. The to-ing and fro-ing of these years is reminiscent of the final phases of a bad marriage. Beyond a certain point, and with a backlog of resentments that can not be dislodged, the best intentions of both parties are to no avail. The end of the relationship is inevitable.

The irrigation project was proving to be a total disaster for the CPR. Millions of dollars had been sunk into it and reputations staked on its success. Now it had to be acknowledged that neither monetary nor professional returns were to be realized from it. There were other problems with CPR lands administration and in 1933, the president of the company appointed a five-man committee to study the entire operation of the Department of Natural Resources — from its inception in 1912 right up to the current year's activities.

The report resulting from this study made a number of recommendations. Most important, insofar as the Eastern Irrigation District is concerned, is "No. 4." It states,

> That the gradual abandonment of the Western Section of the irrigation block
> be continued; and that in the Eastern Section every effort should be made to
> promote the organization of an Irrigation District with a view to transfer of the
> system, but that abandonment should not presently be considered.

Although the report was not given the final approval by the Executive Committee of the Board of Directors of the CPR until the end of March, 1934, George Walker, who was a member of the committee that made the recommendation, was certain of its acceptance. At a meeting late in 1933, he dropped a hint of its contents, with respect to the Eastern Section, to Carl Anderson.

Walker was described as an astute gentlemen with an instinctive ability to judge human behavior. He realized that shifting of responsibility for the irrigation system from the CPR to the farmers would be a delicate business. It was by no means a foregone conclusion that the majority would accept such an obligation and, if they refused it, the CPR would be morally bound to continue to operate the system. It would take someone from among the farmers to lead the way.

Walker chose his man wisely. Carl Anderson, a man of 37 at the time, was possessed of energy to spare. He had a certain charisma. Not everyone loved him but almost everyone repected him. And, he had the courage to take an idea whose time had come and run with it. He showed this characteristic in his own farming operation. He was one of the first to go into livestock and was instrumental in organizing a livestock shipping association among his neighbours.

Anderson was stunned by the magnitude of what Walker had suggested to him. Could a group of farmers take over and manage effectively the same irrigation system on which a large and powerful company was losing money? As he pondered this possibility, the idea gradually took hold of him, and it never let go, no matter what the difficulties, until the Eastern Irrigation District was born, almost two years later.

THE IDEA OF AN IRRIGATION DISTRICT TAKES HOLD

Once Anderson was committed and was assured of the support of an inner circle, he carefully planned how best to introduce to the large body of the District UFA the notion of a farmer takeover. First, he launched the idea at home on the Bow Slope. As he feared, the members of his Local thought he had gone mad. Fortunately, when he went to the Rainier UFA to broach the idea, there was an older man in his audience, a Mr. Stuhlsatz, who pointed out that, since the district was in such a depressed state, there was little to lose by investigating the possibility of improving their position by taking on responsibility for their own water system.

With this vote of approval, Anderson went back to Scandia and persuaded his own friends and neighbours to draft a resolution of the proposition to the District UFA. This happened in February of 1934.

Acceptance was not immediate but, bit by bit, from that point on, the farmers were won over. From outright rejection of the proposition they began to move toward a cautious recognition that perhaps the impossible could be achieved.

From September 1934 until the transfer of the system was accomplished, *The Brooks Bulletin* printed open letters from the District UFA committees to keep farmers in the area apprised of the negotiations.

A committee of 17 of the District Association's members was assigned to conduct a feasibility study. This demanded the personal sacrifice of many hours stolen from farming operations but its results were encouraging.

The decision was reached in the fall of 1934, after the harvest was in, that a small committee of three should be elected to negotiate with the CPR, seek government assistance and report back to the main body of the organization.

A well-attended District meeting on November 1st went on from morning until evening. L. C. Charlesworth of the Alberta Irrigation Council was on hand to

answer questions regarding farmer-operated irrigation systems. Of 275 people present at the evening session, less than 50 percent exercised their vote. Nevertheless, the small committee was elected — Carl Anderson, William Sheldrake and a third member from the Brooks UFA local, W. Tait White.

Tait White was born in Scotland in 1884 and came to Calgary in 1904 to seek out opportunities in a new country. He worked on the construction of the irrigation system in the CPR's Western Section and later on land reclassification in that district.

In 1915, he went overseas with the Canadian Expeditionary Force, rose to the rank of major and was awarded the Merit Cross for bravery. After the war, White settled on a farm west of Brooks.

The three-man committee was undertaking a mammoth task. To assist them on their way, a collection was taken up among the UFA members, which yielded $40 expense money for the Small Committee. On top of paying for trips to Calgary to negotiate with the CPR, the money had to cover the costs incurred in four months of running about from place to place within the district to inform farmers of their progress.

Tait White had been put in charge of the $40; and by the time the final deal was struck with the CPR, months later, he still had several dollars left in the treasury — courtesy, no doubt, of his Scottish background!

Negotiations between the Small Committee and the CPR went forward amicably enough. George Walker was the main negotiator for the CPR. C. H. Powlett, who had been on Walker's staff for several years and had done much of the legal work concerning the Eastern Section, left the employ of the CPR, with Walker's blessing, to act as legal counsel for the water users' group.

His was an interesting deal with his new employers. If the transfer of the system to the farmers was carried through successfully, he was to be paid twice the fee he would have charged had the farmers had any money. In the event that the deal fell through, he would receive no compensation for his efforts. With these conditions attached, Powlett worked very hard. Although $10,000 seemed a small fortune in 1935, the newly-formed Eastern Irrigation District paid the bill in full with the conviction that they had been well-served.

The CPR offered to make full disclosure of their financial records to the Provincial Auditor. The farmers' group sought further assistance from the government through the Irrigation Council. They wanted expert assurance that the structures of the irrigation system were in good order. The consulting engineer retained for the latter job was none other than Hugh B. Muckleston, who had been the system's designer. He gave the structures a clean bill of health, and must have felt some pride that they were still doing so well, after over twenty years' service.

THE FIRST DEAL

Pending the results of the audit, a tentative deal was made between the CPR and the Small Committee. It was at this time that intensive promotional work began. The members of the 17-member Large Committee, who were representative of the entire district, arranged for farmers to gather in each of the communities; and the Small Committee, with their lawyer, travelled from place to place laying out the proposed plan. These meetings occurred in the dead of winter, and attendant problems of poor vehicles, treacherous roads and blizzards plagued their travels.

The plan they put forward to the farmers consisted of these particulars: the farmers would assume ownership of all the existing contracts, all of the unsold lands in the irrigation block, and the entire delivery system, with total responsibility for its maintenance and operation. For all of this, the water users would pay the CPR $500,000-$25,000 per year for 20 years with no interest. The face value of the complete package they were to purchase was $20 million.

If an irrigation district were formed as the Small Committee proposed, all of the individual indebtedness would be wiped out and new land contracts would be negotiated, with the top price per acre set at no more than $10. It was estimated that overhead could be radically reduced and that water rates, which might be somewhat higher than under the CPR, would cover the costs of general operation and maintenance. This was the inducement offered the farmers.

Although most were receptive to the plan, opposition grew up, based largely upon a feeling that the Small Committee would succeed in catapulting the water users into an onerous deal without having all the evidence before them. The Small Committee's response to this criticism was that the government was investigating the entire situation and they would not pass the legislation to enable the water users to form an irrigation district unless they felt it could be operated successfully.

In spite of the fact that he stomped the district with White, Anderson and Powlett, putting the first proposal forward for the consideration of the farmers, Bill Sheldrake must have had nagging doubts about it. Or perhaps he had less trust than the others in the wisdom of government officials. When many of the people he had worked with and respected in the Duchess area formed the Contract Holders' Protective Association to oppose takeover of the system under the current plan, Sheldrake withdrew from the Small Committee.

In an open letter printed in *The Brooks Bulletin* on January 31, 1935, Sheldrake filed his minority report. In it, he stated that responsibility for delivering water to the farms of the project was a sufficient price to pay and that, if the farmers were to take it on, they should do so without any financial encumbrance. He said the irrigation project was a "red ink proposition" and that the CPR should pay the water users $150,000 to cover operating expenses in the transition period necessary to put the irrigation district on its feet. He felt there would be no justification for making "a bargain that is impractical [just] because the government may support our plans."

It is ironic that the final agreement struck between the CPR and the water users was closely in accord with Sheldrake's proposal, although he had retired from the fray and was not in on the closing of the agreement. Harry Jones from Bassano was elected to take Sheldrake's place on the Small Committee. Jones was born in Missouri and, although he moved west to Washington as a young man, he never lost his measured drawl. He came to Alberta in 1910 to homestead in the Jenner area. When this venture proved unrewarding, he decided to hire out his farming and ranching expertise. While working in the Bassano area,

Jones met and married Gertrude McConaughey, a widow and landowner there. They continued to farm in the irrigated area around Bassano, while adding grassland south of the Bow River to their holdings. Over the years, they built up a substantial farming and ranching operation.

The proposal put forward by the Contract Holders' Protective Association was much less measured than Sheldrake's. To have met their demands, the CPR would have had to continue to operate and maintain the main canal system and major structures, transfer to the farmers' group all land and equipment and, at a cost of $1.00 each, give all contract holders title to their lands. The Protective Association was prepared, in exchange, to operate and maintain the secondary canal system. This group was later to claim credit for the final deal with the CPR but it is doubtful they were justified in doing so.

Voting for the proposal to form an irrigation district was scrupulously conducted under the supervision of the Irrigation Council. Petition forms were made available to all farmers so that they could register their votes for or against the proposal. The votes were to be submitted to the Minister in Charge of Administration of the Irrigation District Act by February 1st, 1935. It was an issue that should have been of primary importance to everyone in the area, so it is surprising that, of the 759 contract holders, only a few more than 60% registered an opinion. Of these, more than 80% were in favour of the formation of an irrigation district.

Consummation of the deal between the CPR and the Small Committee seemed near at hand. All it awaited was the government's blessing. And then, the provincial auditor's report arrived and, as Carl Anderson puts it, it was "as if a mule had kicked us in the stomach and set us on our backsides." A very thorough search of the CPR's books had shown that operating losses on the irrigation system were much higher than the farmers' committee had understood from the figures furnished them earlier.

When Anderson, White and Jones had recovered sufficiently from the shock of the auditor's findings, they wrote to S. G. Porter, manager of the CPR-DNR to say that, as far as the Small Committee was concerned, the deal was off. That is, unless the CPR was willing to advance the farmers $400,000, in view of the heavy operating losses suffered by the system over the past six years. The other demand, thrown in for good measure on Powlett's advice, was that the CPR waive the stipulation that the irrigation district would be liable for any damage done to the structures of the railway by the water system. This latter concession, relieving the District of what might have been a serious onus, was incorporated in the final agreement with the CPR.

Disheartened and ashamed of the enthusiasm with which they had promoted the transfer of the system to their friends and neighbours, the Small Committee was sure an impasse had been reached. They were surprised when a wire arrived from George Walker, who recently had been promoted and transferred to Montreal. He requested that they meet him in Calgary a few days hence. This was in early March of 1935.

THE SECOND (AND FINAL) DEAL

The meeting began in a white heat as Anderson went on the offensive. He accused the company of having given misleading figures to the farmers. He said they were not interested in explanations of how operating losses can be hidden in capital expenditure columns. All they had asked from the CPR was the actual amount spent on operating and maintaining the irrigation system. Anderson's outburst seemed to amuse Walker, who said to his colleagues, "I guess he settled your hash!" From that point on, most of the negotiating was done between Anderson and Walker.

They were worthy adversaries. Anderson demanded $400,000. After several hours of debate, Walker offered $100,000. Anderson refused the offer. They broke for supper and, at 8:00 p.m., they were back at the bargaining table. By 9:00, Walker was worn down to the point of agreeing that the CPR would pay $200,000. Anderson balked and redoubled his efforts to gain twice that figure. The battle was to and fro. Then, as the hands of the clock approached midnight, Walker offered $300,000 and vowed that was his final figure. A consultation among the committee and their legal counsel was held in the hall outside the meeting room. Anderson, nothing if not stubborn, wanted to hold out for the full price of $400,000. Powlett knew Walker well and advised they would not be likely to wring more money from him. White and Jones were in agreement that $300,000 would see the irrigation district through its first year but they wanted to return to the meeting room with a unanimous decision. Anderson relented, and the deal was done.

Tired but jubilant, the Small Committee made their triumphal journey home. The borrowed car they rode in had ill-fitting doors through which seeped the bitter cold of early March. But physical discomfort could not daunt their spirits, now. They were carrying news to their fellow farmers of a deal far more beneficial to the community than anyone could have anticipated, back when the long and difficult struggle to improve their lot began.

When the farmers were informed of the new deal made with the CPR on their behalf, they were in full accord. Even the Contract Holders' Protective Association could no longer find fault with the Small Committee's success, so they quickly wired their acceptance of the agreement to the government in Edmonton.

The Irrigation Council, in the person of L. C. Charlesworth, had followed the Small Committee's negotiations with interest and had been ready with advice and encouragement throughout the period leading up to the final deal. Charlesworth now prepared a comprehensive brief for the Minister of Agriculture, F. S. Grisdale, in which he described the irrigation project, its history and current status. He recommended the immediate framing of legislation to expedite the transfer of the irrigation block from the CPR to the farmers' organization. Subsequently, the Eastern Irrigation District Act was passed; and on May 1, 1935, one of the foremost irrigation schemes on the North American continent was transferred lock, stock and barrel to the local farmers.

PART III
THE FIRST FIFTY YEARS
1935-1985

Wintered on dry land, cattle and sheep ford the South Saskatchewan River on the way to summer grazing in the EID. Photographer: James Newton.

THE HONEYMOON PERIOD

Once the Eastern Irrigation District actually became established in 1935, the first orders of business involved organization of the machinery that would guarantee its effective operation. The authority for such procedures was given under both the EID Act and the Irrigation Districts Act. The latter statute, first passed in 1915, made provision for a group of water users to form a corporation, known as an irrigation district, for the purpose of owning and operating their own water delivery system. Under the Act, each district was autonomous. The water users were to elect a board of trustees to conduct their business. The board was to number from three to seven members, depending upon the amount of irrigable land in the district. To advise the board on the conduct of its affairs and to authorize by-laws, financing, and construction projects, an Irrigation Council of up to three members was appointed by the Lieutenant-Governor-in-Council. Maintenance standards were the responsibility of the district. A quasi-municipal status allowed for operating expenses to be raised through the levying of water rates against the irrigable holdings of each water user.

Special acts were passed subsequent to the Act of 1915, to cover specific conditions under which individual districts were formed. Such an act was the Eastern Irrigation District Act of 1935, which was required to ratify the agreement made between the CPR and the farmers. It dealt with the peculiar status of the EID as landowner, imposing certain restrictions on the disposition of land. For instance, the Irrigation Council had to be assured that a potential purchaser of land in the EID was capable of farming competently, before the board of trustees could sell to him.

Charlesworth, representing the Irrigation Council, was appointed official trustee of the new EID until such time as a three-man board of trustees could be elected. Some of their fellow farmers put forward the names of the Small Committee members to stand for election. The Contract Holders' Protective Association, claiming credit for the final deal made with the CPR, rallied its forces and selected three opposing contenders for positions of trusteeship. Perhaps the electoral machine of the latter group was more persuasive than that behind the Small Committee. In any case, when the elections were held on May 25, 1935, two of their nominees, Henry Dahl of Duchess and Robert Scott of Tilley, were victorious. Of the three men who had worked with such diligence for the formation of the EID, only Carl Anderson, who garnered a large majority of the total votes cast, was elected. Such are the vicissitudes of politics!

THE GOOD NEWS

To their credit, once elected, Dahl and Scott worked harmoniously with Carl Anderson, the chairman of the board. In the face of an overwhelmingly large work load, petty disagreements were put aside and the board turned to the tasks at hand. Foremost among these was the hiring of a general manager. From among the three candidates put forward by the Irrigation Council, the board chose a rising young civil servant. E. L. Gray resigned his position as Deputy Minister of Municipal

Affairs to accept the exciting challenge of launching a new irrigation district, and reported for work on September 1, 1935.

True to their word, the board of trustees and their new manager put the matter of renegotiation of the farmers' land contracts before all other business. Progress was hampered somewhat by requests from some of the water users for reclassification of their land. This necessitated inspection by EID staff of over 62,000 acres, (25,110 ha) and resulted in 14,364 acres (5,817 ha) being classified as unsuitable for irrigation and taken off the water rolls. By the end of 1936, fresh contracts had been drawn up with all of the water users. In these, the value of irrigable land was set at $10 or less per acre ($4 per ha), an 80 per cent reduction from the original price set by the CPR.

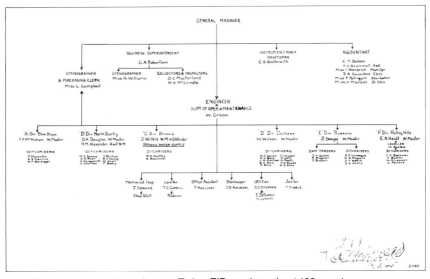

1945 EID staff chart — 64 employees. Today, EID employs about 100 people.

The staff for operating and maintenance was pared by 50 per cent; and high overhead costs, which had been sustained throughout the CPR days, were radically reduced. At the first annual meeting of the EID, the board was proud to report that, to cover operating costs in the transitional year, it had not been necessary to use any of the $300,000 reserve fund. In fact, revenues from water rates had covered all costs, with some $6,000 to spare. This, despite the fact that reclassification had led to an estimated loss of more than $20,000 in water rates.

Such success was beyond all expectations. The farmers of the District must indeed have felt that they were at the beginning of an era in a brave new world. The following two years brought continued progress and resulted in a general feeling of confidence in the abilities of the board and the general manager.

Foremost among the accomplishments of the first four years of operation was the increase in irrigable acreage. The 90,000 acres (36,450 ha) which were actually irrigated in 1935 had been increased, by almost 50 per cent, to 134,000

CANADIAN PACIFIC RAILWAY COMPANY
DEPARTMENT OF NATURAL RESOURCES
S G PORTER, MANAGER   A. GRIFFIN, CHIEF ENGINEER

STAFF CHART

EASTERN SECTION ENGINEERING BRANCH

A. GRIFFIN   SUPT. OPER'N. & MAINTENANCE
F. G. CROSS   ASS'T. SUPT. OPER'N. & MAINTENANCE

BROOKS HEADQUARTERS

J F ROSS — SUPERINTENDENT

OFFICE STAFF

C T SCHON	CHIEF CLERK
H C SCAMMELL	ACCOUNTANT
MISS S. WEST	STENOGRAPHER

OUTSIDE STAFF

F W GIBSON	STOREKEEPER
F H BERRY	ASST. STOREKEEPER
N SWANSON	BLACKSMITH
D MACPHERSON	BLACKSMITH
W A PHILLPOTT	SHOP CARPENTER
J GRAY	FARM FOREMAN
R McARRASHER	YARD MAN
J W OWENS	GARDENER

DRAINAGE INVESTIGATION

P M BETH — LEVELLER
(3) V L WINTER — ASST HYDROG & LEVELLER

MECHANICAL

C M CHALMERS	MECHANICAL SUPT.
C C STEPHEN	MECHANIC
L TURNER	MACHINIST
W KEAY	GARAGE FOREMAN
F D BROWN	MECHANIC
R ROMNEY	MECHANIC
V NELSON	MECHANIC
R J BAXTER	NIGHTWATCHMAN

SURVEYS AND ENG'R'G.

C M DENISON	OFFICE ENGINEER
(3) T C CAPELL	DRAFTSMAN
F W HUGHES	LEVELLER
N M ALEXANDER	RODMAN

ADMINISTRATIVE DIVISIONS

DUCHESS DIVISION

C C ELLIOTT	CANAL SUPT.
T F McMAHON	ASST WATERMASTER

DITCHRIDERS	RESERVATION
H AUER	KOKAY
J T KINGSTON	DUCHESS
P MILLER	WELCH
J C SALSER	WILKINS
J BROWN	McKENZIE
F J CLARKE	BAKER
J McHALE	COCKERILL
G H MATTHEWS	HAFFNER
J P ARUNDELL (4)	IMPERIAL

TELEPHONES AND ELECTRICAL EQUIPMENT

T SCHULTE (2)	SUPERINTENDENT
G E QUIRIN (2)	INSPECTOR
T H MILLSON (2)	INSPECTOR
C E R LAMBERT (2)	LINE FOREMAN
MRS. L CLAY	OPERATOR

BROOKS BOWSLOPE DIV.

F Y ARCHIBALD	CANAL SUPT.
W CROOK	ASST WATERMASTER

DITCHRIDERS	RESERVATION
J STEVENTON	RAINIER
W F DUMONT	GREENTREE
W N BRANDLE	ROSS
S O MERRICK	KITSIM
J C WILKIE	BROOKS
T E KAY	ANT. CREEK SYPHON
L NELSON	CASSILS SYPHON

BANTRY DIVISION

G H RICHARDSON	CANAL SUPT.
F G REBITT	LEVELLER ASST'G d₀
H C BROWN	ASST WATERMASTER

DITCHRIDERS	RESERVATION
M J DUNNE	AQUEDUCT
G H GILES	CONOKA
E J BEISIEGEL	SAND CREEK
S IRELAND	MILLICENT
J W ENGLISH	GILBERTSON
S WARD	PATRICIA
K RUST	WEST BANTRY
A JUDGE	ELIZABETH

BASSANO DIVISION

H G ANGELL	CANAL SUPT.
S C FRENCH	ASST. CANAL SUPT.
S J BROCK	GARAGE FOREMAN
A CADOR	MECHANICS HELPER
J FRASER	DAM MASTER
E PRAGNELL	DAM TENDER
S HENDRICKS	BARN MAN
J SNAPE	WATERMASTER
D K DOUGLAS	ASST WATERMASTER
H WILSON	ASST WATERMASTER

DITCHRIDER	RESERVATION
H A ROSS	LATHOM
J NEWMAN	McLEAN
A LEVESQUE	COUNTESS
E GRATWICK	LITTLE BOW
J B SPARKS	PITRU
T L MAGUIRE	GEM
W J JONES	MANNING BUTTE

2. Not on Eastern Section payroll. Work charged against appropriation.
3. Assigned various duties.
4. Temporary not on staff form.

CORRECT TO NOV. 30, 1933.

O. Griffin

SUPT. OPERATION AND MAINTENANCE

1933 CPR staff chart — 81 employees. Staff was sharply decreased from mid-1920's when about 200 were employed.

acres (54,270 ha) by the 1938 year-end. A continuing policy of selective colonization, coupled with the introduction of electric water pumps and the building of
several new reservoirs, were the primary means used to effect this phenomenal
increase in lands on the water roll. This, in turn, led to increased revenues from the
collection of water rates and put the District on sound financial footing. The
District's fourth annual report shows an operating surplus of over $48,000 and a
reserve fund for replacement of capital structures valued at $1.4 million. Not bad
for a bunch of shovel-wielding irrigation farmers!

As befits what was then referred to as a co-operative organization, the EID
also began inaugurating new programs and services which the board and general
manager believed would prove of great benefit to all ratepayers. A hail insurance
fund was instituted, so that farmers could still pay their water rates, even if they got
hailed out. This program was operated by the District on an almost-continuous
basis until 1974, when the farmers were asked to switch to the provincial hail
insurance scheme.

In the late 1930's, the District began a policy of "assisting settlers to procure
livestock for fattening purposes." To accomplish this, the District would buy large
numbers of livestock at a good price in the fall of the year, and then distribute them
to local farmers for feeding and fattening over the winter. The following spring,
the stock were resold and the District reimbursed. Through this program, the
farmer received both a market for his hay and feed grain, and a source of cash
income with which he could pay his water rates and other bills.

As the CPR had done before them, the new board and staff encouraged
farmers to diversify into livestock and specialty crops. They also spoke of
encouraging agricultural processing industries to locate in the District, thus
providing a ready market for local produce. Area residents had expected that a
sugar beet factory would be established in Brooks "any day" during 1930 and
1931, but their hopes had been dashed. The idea cropped up again in the mid-
Thirties. Sugar beet enthusiasts hoped that this time, with a dedicated board of
trustees and zealous manager, the project would actually get off the ground.

E. L. GRAY

It has been said that E. L. Gray was bound up
in the early success of the EID. Certainly, the
driving force of his energy was an impetus. A
farmer's son from Saskatchewan, Edward Leslie
Gray attended agricultural college in both Manitoba and Ontario before coming to Alberta in
the 1920's to teach at the Claresholm School of
Agriculture.

In 1927, he moved to Hanna to take up a
position as what would now be called a district
agriculturalist. He became Alberta's first Field
Crops Commissioner in 1930. In 1934, he left
the Department of Agriculture, but continued his
civil service career as Deputy Minister of Municipal Affairs — the position he left
to take up managership of the fledgling EID.

It must have been very exciting for Gray to be in on the ground floor of such a potentially prosperous project. But Gray seems to have been a man who needed more action than any one job, no matter how many-faceted, could provide. The thrust and parry of provincial politics interested him greatly and the summer of 1937 saw him assume the leadership of the Alberta Liberal party. The board of trustees had given permission for him to undertake this involvement, but only on the understanding that he would not subsequently let his name stand for election to the Assembly. Perhaps they later felt that a manager with political influence could not hurt the District and might, in fact, be in a position to help it progress. In any case, the board did not stand in Gray's way when, in the fall of the same year, he decided to contest a seat in an Edmonton by-election.

Within the first few months of his service as an MLA, the board became concerned that Gray was not able to devote sufficient time and energy to his first commitment, that of running the affairs of the EID. Nonetheless, Gray continued to wear three hats. He was, at one and the same time, the general manager of the EID, leader of the Liberal party, and Edmonton MLA until February 10, 1939, at which time the Board accepted his resignation.

On the same date, they appointed Lionel C. Charlesworth, then provincial Director of Water Resources and the sole member of the Irrigation Council, to succeed Gray. Charlesworth, an articulate and knowledgeable man, was retiring from the civil service at the end of March. His advice and counsel had often been helpful to the board and, no doubt, its members were pleased to secure the services of such an experienced individual. They expected that his appointment would enhance the District's prestige. Unfortunately, events unfolded in such a way that Charlesworth did not actively assume the role of general manager until December 6 — almost eight full months after the date on which he had originally agreed to report for duty. But, more on this subject later. First, it is necessary to set the scene for the play of circumstances that conspired to confuse the orderly succession of EID general managers.

THE BAD NEWS: INHERITED PROBLEMS

When the Eastern Irrigation District was formed in 1935, it inherited a number of things from the CPR: the water system, a $300,000 reserve fund, and several sets of problems. As well, the District inherited an attitude, which was widespread among its residents — that, as the CPR had always done, the EID would assume responsibility for a great many services that had little or nothing to do with water delivery. For instance, in an effort to provide a reliable and consistent source of factual information about District business, the board contracted with *The Brooks Bulletin* to take out paid subscriptions for all water users. In return, the local weekly agreed to reserve space for printing of EID policies and developments.

Gradually, of course, it became obvious to the EID staff, the board of trustees and, eventually, to the majority of residents that it was financially impossible for the District to continue to operate in so paternalistic a fashion. With this realization, individuals and communities began to undertake more responsibility for utilities and other services. In the meantime, despite its comparatively miniscule revenue from water rates, the EID tried to continue many of the programs put in place by the CPR, who had a very large corporate budget from which to operate.

TAXES

One of the first problems to surface was that of taxes assessed by the local improvement districts and school districts. Early in its operation, the EID discovered that the CPR had been charging only three cents per acre annual rent for its grazing lands, while paying taxes of ten cents per acre. It was obvious to the board that they could not afford such a loss. As they did not believe they would be successful in obtaining a re-assessment of the grasslands tax, the board decided to sell as much of this land as possible. This was a boon to local ranchers and farmers, who were able to purchase large areas of grazing land for as little as five cents an acre. These land deals provided the revenue for the District to pay the taxes on their remaining holdings. Eventually, political pressure brought to bear on the Department of Municipal Affairs by the individual local ranchers resulted in a more equitable tax rate on grasslands.

ROADS AND BRIDGES

A second major difficulty was related to the construction and maintenance of bridges and culverts. In 1934, a Bridge Agreement was made between the CPR and the provincial government, in which the responsibilities of each party were outlined. When the EID took over the CPR interests, it expected to fulfill the railway company's obligations under the contract.

Short months after the District's formation, the UFA government, with whom the original agreement had been made, was ousted from office. Its successor, the Social Credit government, refused to honour its responsibilities in the matter. Accordingly, the District found itself wholly responsible for the costs of building, as well as maintaining and rebuilding, many local bridges, and even some roads.

Brooks-Scandia road. Deterioration of bridge across Bow Slope Canal, 1954.

Until the late 1940's, the local improvement district owned very little heavy equipment, so the EID was forced to come to the rescue, using its machines and operators for many tasks which, in other parts of the province, were being paid for with municipal funds. In order to ensure that water users could get their products to market, the EID did its utmost to make local roads passable.

The agricultural recession of the 1950's, coupled with year after year of bad weather, put the District in a financial squeeze. It could not continue to provide a service it believed to be a provincial responsibility.

In 1957, the board and general manager put aside their time-honoured attitude that government had no business in District affairs, and they sought financial assistance for bridge construction and maintenance of irrigation structures. But to no avail. Proposals and counter-proposals went back and forth for more than three years. In the meantime, the situation was further complicated by an increase in road traffic; more and heavier vehicles were using the roads with increasing frequency.

Finally, in 1960, the Board decided to pull out all the stops. They sent the Department of Highways a bill for over a quarter of a million dollars. That figure represented the province's share of District bridge expenditures since 1935.

Several more years of negotiation, culminating with EID threats to sue for compensation, finally moved the government to institute a schedule for shared responsibility. The Road Authority of the Department of Highways was to accept the duty of maintaining bridges and highways over large canals, as of March 31, 1965. The District would retain responsibility for bridges on local roads over smaller canals.

Through the Alberta Irrigation Projects Association, other irrigation districts were making similar demands for assistance. Since 1969, bridges are included among the structures for which the provincial government has committed funds to irrigation districts for rehabilitation. According to a cost-sharing formula, 86 per cent of reconstruction costs are borne by the Department of Agriculture; the remaining 14 per cent is the onus of the irrigation district.

UTILITIES: WATER, POWER, TELEPHONES

In order to carry out its own operations, the CPR had built several utilities in the Eastern Section, which were turned over to the EID in 1935. Gradually, these were phased out of service.

One of the first to go, in 1941, was the noisy Brooks town irrigation pump. Next came the power generating plants at Bassano Dam and Brooks townsite. They were taken over by Calgary Power in 1951.

Two other utilities, the town water supply in Brooks and the area's telephone system, were operated by the District until well into the 1960's. As was the case with most of the towns along its rail line, the CPR provided Brooks with a water distribution system. Initially, there were two water towers: a larger one on the north side of the tracks near the station, designed to serve the CPR locomotives; and a smaller one, which still stands on the south side of "Brooks slough," designed to serve the headquarters buildings and the townsite.

After 1935, the EID supplied domestic and industrial water to Brooks and to the CPR. The water was stored in a large reservoir and then pumped to the water tower. Before the advent of large pumping systems, storage in the water tower built up the pressure necessary to operate the system. The Town of Brooks took over ownership and control of the water distribution network in 1966 — all except for that in EID headquarters which was owned and operated independently until 1984.

No longer used on a daily basis, the old water tower is still maintained in working order and is available for emergencies. Since 1966, all water used in Brooks has been pumped from Lake Newell, eliminating the need for a separate storage reservoir.

The CPR had developed an extensive private telephone network to facilitate communications with its far-flung water districts. After 1935, one of the first economy measures of the new EID was the sale to Alberta Government Telephones of the exchanges at Brooks and Bassano. The number of telephone "instruments" was reduced by 50 per cent. The District did, however, continue to operate a rather extensive network of rural circuits, serving the watermasters and ditchriders.

This situation prevailed for a time. Then, in the 1940's, the District's responsibility for telephone service was again widened. Several mutural telephone systems, co-operatives formed to serve rural subscribers, found themselves in financial straits, and turned to the EID for assistance. The EID complied by buying them out and adding their circuitry to its own system.

When automatic telephones were introduced in 1953, the EID owned and operated 343 of the old magneto telephones on more than 500 miles of lines. This meant that District staff was employed to collect monthly telephone rentals and carry out all of the accounting procedures this entailed.

The physical equipment of the telephone system had deteriorated to the point where, as one of those charged to maintain it said, the wire was holding up the poles. Reconstruction was expensive and, not surprisingly, the telephone system lost money.

By the mid-1950's, the District began to systematically phase out of the telephone business. Mutuals, which had all but disappeared in the 1940's, were formed once again. Soon, they were operating in all parts of the District. By 1965, the EID had rid itself of all but one rural circuit — that to its remote ditchrider location at Cowoki. There were a few EID-owned lines and phones in Brooks until the 1970's when all service was taken over by AGT and underground cable installed.

PAYMENT IN KIND

One of the CPR practices, which frustrated many of its contract holders, was the taking of "payment in kind" (shares of crop or livestock) in lieu of land payments and water rates. From the landowner's point of view, it was a method for getting some return from water users who were unable to make cash payments. On the other hand, from the contract holder's point of view, the result was that the status of the family often sank to that of tenant farmers or sharecroppers. Morale deteriorated, as hope of ever owning their land waned.

Despite their disapproval of the CPR's use of crop-sharing, the EID board and management early found themselves involved in similar programs. They sometimes instituted crop-share leases as a preliminary to sale contracts. This practice was continued, for about a decade, as a way of encouraging colonization of the project. Even those without cash were given the opportunity of settling here and then working toward land-ownership. Most were successful in obtaining sales contracts within two or three years of their arrival.

This policy was successful, in that much of the available land was settled while it was in force; but, it was not without negative aspects. For one thing, the EID staff was involved in taking assignments of water users' crops and livestock, and then marketing them, in order to realize any returns from some land contracts. By 1939, this policy had resulted in losses of $21,000.

When L. C. Charlesworth took over as general manager in late 1940, he drastically reduced the number of crop-sharing leases. These dropped from 347 in 1940 to only 65 in 1944. Of those still in effect, 29 were in the newly-settled Rolling Hills area. A few years later, crop-sharing was completely phased out of the District's affairs.

FARM OPERATIONS

In the manner of the CPR, the EID had begun the practice of operating and improving farmlands until such time as they could be sold. This had resulted in an expenditure of funds on a scale that a lean organization, such as the EID, could ill afford. Efforts were stepped up to divest the District of these holdings. In 1938, there were six EID-owned and -operated farms. By 1943, the last of these had been sold.

THE POLITICAL CLIMATE

After years of hatred for the CPR, the water users of the young Eastern Irrigation District experienced the euphoria that comes with having cast off the yoke of outside authority. Bolstered by early successes, they were firm in the belief that, at long last, the reins of the District were in their own hands. Never again would they relinquish control. This heady confidence was severely shaken in the fourth year of the EID's existence. Without warning, the provincial government insinuated itself into District affairs, ferreting out sensitive areas and then prodding at them, in an attempt to inflame public opinion against the manager and board of trustees.

Most citizens were shocked; they had been prepared to tolerate the obligatory degree of government influence over the District, but this was an outrage! The officers they had deputized to run their affairs were charged with having committed "serious irregularities." To the water users, the charge was applicable to the government, not to the EID. They quickly aligned themselves behind the board and manager.

The confrontation, precipitated because of the government's accusatory position, could just as easily have been averted by a calm exchange among reasonable men. Perhaps some light may be shed on the government's inexplicable behaviour with a capsulized account of Alberta's prevailing political climate and the Social Credit government's record up to 1938.

Shortly after the EID's formation, a provincial election was held in Alberta. The incumbent UFA government went down to an overwhelming defeat at the hands of a new political-religious movement, the Alberta Social Credit League. The leader of the group was William "Bible Bill" Aberhart, a high school principal from Calgary, who had become well-known across the province for his Sunday radio broadcasts from the Prophetic Bible Institute.

Good turnout at Brooks for Social Credit rally, 1935.   Photographer: S. Alberts.

Social Credit economic theory became a growing part of Aberhart's sermons throughout the early 1930's and, by the time the election was called, most Albertans had heard of Aberhart's promised monthly dividends of $25 per family. To the masses of urban unemployed and drought-stricken farm families, it must have seemed that Aberhart would lead them out of the Depression wilderness and into a prosperous Promised Land. In August 1935, the voters elected Social Creditors in all but seven of the 63 constituencies.

After more than three years of Social Credit rule, the Promised Land appeared, to all but Aberhart's most dedicated followers, to be as far off as ever. No dividends had been paid. Taxes had been increased. Most legislation based upon Social Credit principles had been ruled unconstitutional by the courts. One MLA, the government whip, had been found guilty of criminal libel and of counselling to murder. The indictment brought against him was a result of his involvement in the publication of a pamphlet, wherein members of the opposition were described as "bankers' toadies" and "creepy, crawly things." He was sentenced to three months' hard labour in Fort Saskatchewan jail. There had been a major insurrection against Aberhart which involved one-third of the Socred caucus. Vigorous campaigning by Aberhart and his top aides was of little help to the Social Credit League of Saskatchewan. Only two of their candidates were elected in the provincial election of 1938.

Despite the Social Credit's inability to fulfill its campaign promises, the resultant plunge in popular support, and the fact that his party was in disarray, Aberhart, in the course of his regular Sunday broadcast, was able to say, "I'm dead, but I won't lie down." Later that year, he stated unequivocally that his government would serve out its entire five-year term.

The events in the Eastern Irrigation District, in late 1938 and early 1939, caused further loss of face for Aberhart and his government. But the memory of the voting population is notoriously short. By the time the 1940 election rolled around, an economic turnaround that accompanied World War II was in full swing. Few any longer had a need for Aberhart's $25 hand-out. The Social Credit party was returned to power.

"SERIOUS IRREGULARITIES"

Let us back-track now to the year 1938 and examine the sequence of events that led ultimately to a judicial inquiry into the operations of the Eastern Irrigation District.

Imbued with their mission to make the EID a resounding success, the trustees and manager worked hard and seldom deviated from their joint aim. However, as we mentioned earlier, a collection of problems inherited from the days of the CPR sometimes led them to inaugurate slightly unorthodox procedures. As rookies in the irrigation district business, they were certain that their actions would benefit the District, and blithely unaware that any course they adopted to further this cause could possibly be construed as a "serious irregularity."

Reports of their activities eventually reached the ears of the provincial cabinet, with the result that, in November 1938, one Mr. Plunkett, Deputy Provincial Auditor, was instructed by the Provincial Treasurer, Solon E. Low, to conduct an interim audit of the EID's records.

In Plunkett's opinion, irregularities had occurred. Briefly, the board of trustees was alleged to have overstepped its statutory powers with regard to certain loans, land transactions and the formation of a subsidiary company. Various other expenditures were also questioned. Many of these undertakings had not received prior approval from the Irrigation Council.

Charlesworth, in his capacity as the sole member of the Council, was then directed by Low to ask District officers for satisfactory explanations of their actions. This was done in early January of 1939. Charlesworth reported to Hon. D. B. Mullen, Minister of Agriculture and Minister-in-charge of Irrigation, in a letter of January 27:

> I am satisfied, after considering in full all the information available, that while the statutory powers of the Board may have been exceeded to some degree, whatever was done was undertaken in an effort to benefit the project . . . the members of the Board are intelligent, active successful farmers of the district. The welfare of the district means their welfare. They were without doubt endeavoring to improve the position of the district in the interests of the water users.

The board and general manager had wanted "to have a full discussion on the question in order to avoid any possible criticism in future." Now, they believed that Charlesworth's report and a follow-up meeting they had with the Irrigation Council in February would clear the air and bring the matter to a satisfactory close. But they were so wrong!

THE TRIBULATION

The first indication that the provincial government did not intend to tactfully withdraw came when the trustees were contacted by the Irrigation Council on March 17 with a peremptory invitation to attend a conference in Edmonton the following day: Saturday, March 18. In addition to Charlesworth, who had been its sole member for many years, the Irrigation Council had suddenly been augmented threefold. Its new members were the Hon. D. B. Mullen, Minister of Agriculture, and the Hon. Solon E. Low, Provincial Treasurer.

News of this conference was soon picked up by Edmonton and Calgary dailies. In the Saturday editions, speculations as to its purpose and possible outcome were printed. More of the same filled the pages at the first of the week. Then, on Tuesday, the press dropped a bomb shell. The EID Trustees were on their way back to Brooks, confident that the difficulties between them and the government could be resolved. Their composure was rocked when a boy selling newspapers became the inadvertent bearer of bad tidings. Glaring headlines in *The Calgary Albertan* announced their dismissal.

E. I. D. BOARD DISMISSED

OFFICIAL TRUSTEE APPOINTED

Back in Brooks, unbeknownst to the board members, someone else had already been made privy to the government's plan of action. George A. Robertson was then the EID's business superintendent. A former CPR employee, he had stayed on with the District and was known for his ability to organize office procedure and keep careful records. In the early spring twilight of March 21, he received a phone call from Solon Low, who told him that, due to pressure arising from the November audit, the attorney-general had advised the Irrigation Council to proceed with the appointment of an official trustee. It would be this person's duty to be responsible for all the District's affairs and to guide its ship "into safe channels." Low asked Robertson, as someone who knew the District's business well, to take on that responsibility. Apparently, Robertson agreed to do so — on the understanding that an order-in-council would soon be passed, legitimizing his appointment. In the meantime, Low cautioned, he was to "say nothing and do nothing until further instructed."

Before he left the headquarters building, Robertson received three more telephone calls. The first of these was from Low, but E. L. Gray, who was in Low's office at the time, also spoke. After asking that Robertson say nothing "to alarm others," they assured him they'd be in touch by phone and letter. The second call was from Carl Anderson, who, unaware of Low's earlier communications with Robertson, wanted to alert him to the board's dismissal and his own appointment to act in their stead. The final caller, Clive Nesbitt, editor of *The Bulletin*, was sniffing out a story.

On Thursday, March 23, the Lieutenant-Governor passed an order-in-council authorizing the appointment of an official trustee in the EID. The following day, Premier Aberhart made an official statement in which he tried to clarify the government's position vis-à-vis the EID situation. He denied absolutely the earlier press reports that the government's actions were motivated by a wish to take over the EID. Instead, he averred that the report of "serious irregularities by the manager and board of trustees in the formation of subsidiary companies as well as the transactions carried on by these companies" had led to Mr. Robertson's appointment as official trustee. Robertson was to act in that capacity until a thorough investigation had been carried out, after which the water-users would have the opportunity to elect a new board, who would then appoint a general manager to succeed Gray. Aberhart, in direct challenge to Charlesworth's appointment, stated emphatically, "Any announcement that this appointment has been made and approved already is premature and unauthorized."

PROVINCE MA CONTROL BROOKS IRRIGATION BLOCK

LOCAL REACTION

News of the premier's announcement reached Brooks by about noon that same day. The local *Calgary Herald* correspondent described the situation as one in which initial shock was quickly followed by widespread indignation and denunciation of the government's "butting in" to the District's affairs. Within hours of receiving the distressing news, two mass meetings were quickly convened at Brooks, with a total of over 800 area residents in attendance. Allegations of politically-motivated interference were rife. They were based, no doubt, on the

IRREGULARITIES CHARGED

Air Dreadnaughts

Action Follows Auditors' Findings In Brooks Affairs, Says Aberhart; Gray Alleges Crude 'Dirty Politics'

| Claim Local Board Has Exceeded Authority | DISTRICT RALLIES IN QUICK PROTEST OVER GOV'T MOVE | 'Will Be Given Ample Opportunity' To Show Proof |

SUBSIDIARIES

By FRED KENNEDY
(Herald Staff Correspondent)

Edmonton, March 24

As forecast exclusively in last Saturday's editions of the Herald, the provincial government this morning dismissed the board of trustees of the Eastern Irrigation District at Brooks, and appointed

See **Strong Support**
For **Deposed**
Trustees

DENUNCIATION

'DESPICABLE'

Edmonton, March 24

BULLETIN—

A notice of motion for a resolution calling upon the legislature to call a royal commission of inquiry into the affairs of the Eastern Irrigation District at Brooks will be filed in the legislature this afternoon by the Liberal opposition.

Mass Meetings at Brooks Demand E.I.D. Board Be Reinstated at Once Until Government Charges Proved

fact that the District's general manager was also Liberal party leader in the legislative assembly.

Resolutions were passed, indicating that the vast majority of water-users supported the actions of their board and management. At one meeting, originally convened for discussions on the formation of a co-operative, a protest was drafted and forwarded to Mr. Low. After outlining the District's considerable accomplishments, the letter deplores the adverse publicity recently accorded it. It concludes with a very strong statement that "unwarranted" government interference in District affairs will not be tolerated and a request that the message be read immediately to the legislative assembly.

Yet a third meeting was held in Brooks on the same day. Hosted by the Large Committee, it was to have been a celebration of the fourth anniversary of the farmer's takeover of their irrigation project. The event was also intended to serve the dual purpose of a farewell to Mr. Gray and a welcome to Mr. Charlesworth. Ironically, that day of celebration became one in which the District had to face the worst calamity of its short history: the suspension of the board of trustees, and the consequent loss of control over their own affairs.

Will Not Stand For Interference

---◆---

Steady Improvements in Four Years Stressed by Brooks U.F.A. Meeting

HOPES FOR A SPEEDY RESOLUTION

Despite these profoundly disturbing events, the locals continued to be unaware of the far-reaching and long-term consequences of them. The deposed trustees still seemed to believe that the whole affair would be concluded in a month or six weeks. On March 29, they held a meeting at which George Robertson was appointed secretary. To ensure that a general manager would be present to act as returning officer in the upcoming election for one trustee position, the board approved changes to the dates of both Gray's resignation and Charlesworth's commencement. The resignation was to take effect on April 30, while Charlesworth was to begin his new duties May 1. Ironically, it was at this meeting that Robertson also informed the Trustees that he had just received written confirmation of his trusteeship from Mr. Mullen, Minister of Agriculture.

The Annual General Meetings for the 1938 operating year were scheduled for March 31 and April 1, 1939 — in Brooks and Countess respectively. Attendance at both meetings was high and, not unexpectedly, the main topic of conversation was the recent action of the Irrigation Council. Provincial Treasurer Low and Bow Valley MLA Cain were in attendance at the Brooks meeting. They assured the water-users that an investigation into the irregularities would soon be taking place, a full report of which would later be made available to the farmers. At both meetings, motions were made and passd unanimously, thanking Mr. Gray and the board for the way they had been managing the District.

The fifty-two ratepayers who attended the Countess meeting adopted the following resolution:

> Be it resolved that this meeting of water-users instruct Messrs. Carl J. Anderson, Henry Dahl and Robert Scott, as representatives of the water-users do [sic] apply immediately to the Courts, if they feel it necessary, for an injunction to prevent any person or persons other than a Board of Trustees regularly elected by the water-users themselves from taking control of the funds or securities of the Eastern Irrigation District.

But these brave words had little real effect — except perhaps to briefly bolster the confidence of those who heard them. The law clearly stated that the government *did*, indeed, have the legislative authority to appoint an official trustee "at any time and from time to time," thereby causing the board of the district "to cease to hold office."

REFUSAL TO APPROVE CHARLESWORTH'S APPOINTMENT

Another stark reality was that the Irrigation Council could, and did, withhold its approval of Charlesworth's appointment as EID General Manager. Reports in *The Calgary Herald* of March 25 quoted one of the trustees as saying that Low had told them Charlesworth's appointment was not going to be approved. Delicate negotiations with the Montana and Dominion government were underway, and Charlesworth, it was claimed, was the only man who could carry on the work; however, Low apparently failed to persuade Charlesworth that he was indispensable. As planned, the latter left his civil service position at the end of March,

House to Debate Probe Into 'Irregularities' Charged By Aberhart In Management of Irrigation Project

reporting for duty at the EID headquarters building on the morning of April 17, 1939, as per the terms of his contract with the now-ousted board.

That day was, undoubtedly, a momentous one in the life of Mr. Robertson. First thing in the morning Cain, the local MLA, telephoned to see if Charlesworth had taken possession of the manager's office. By noon, Mullen had also called Robertson to state, unequivocally, that Charlesworth's appointment had *not* been approved by the Irrigation Council. With Charlesworth already on deck, this pronouncement put Robertson in a delicate position. Robertson asked Mullen to outline a course of action for him, but Mullen simply repeated his message regarding Charlesworth's non-status.

Doubtless confused by the Minister's reluctance to define the official trustee's duties in the light of such a development, Robertson hopped into his personal car and drove to Medicine Hat for an evening meeting with Mr. Niblock, Barrister and Solicitor, of the firm of Laidlaw, Niblock and Stone. After their consultation, Niblock provided Robertson with a written legal opinion in which it was suggested that the "proper course for you to pursue is to recognize Mr. Charlesworth's contract." After allowing that the contract was a very good one, Niblock went on to argue that since Charlesworth was the *sole* member of the Irrigation Council on February 10, 1939 (the day on which the contract was made), he must have "approved of his own appointment [as EID General-Manager] otherwise he never would have signed the contract."

This was rather cold comfort as Niblock also advised that, should Robertson receive further instruction from the present Irrigation Council (Mullen and Low), he would have no choice but to follow it.

Robertson balanced on the horns of a dilemma until April 19, when he finally received clear instructions from the Minister. He immediately wrote a letter to Charlesworth, marked *"Personal,"* and delivered it to the adjoining office. It reads, virtually word-for-word, the same as Mullen's telegraphed orders to Robertson:

> I am now definitely instructed by the Irrigation Council to advise you that you have no status as Manager of the Eastern Irrigation District and that you must forthwith vacate any desk or office which you may have assumed.

Coincidentally (or perhaps not), Charlesworth was in the country all day, so it was 4:45 p.m. before the official trustee could telegraph the anxious Mullen that Charlesworth had accepted the notification of his dismissal. He would give a written reply the following day.

On the 20th, Mullen was again very pre-occupied with the latest Brooks developments. He wanted to hear of them immediately — if not sooner. At 11:20 a.m. he telegraphed Robertson, "telephone me as soon as you receive a written reply from Mr. Charlesworth." In large letters, at the bottom of the typed telegram Robertson noted: "Phoned 11:45 a.m." Later in the day, he sent Mullen a copy of Charlesworth's letter, which is, rather pointedly, addressed to "George Robertson, Esq., Eastern Irrigation District" and signed, with his distinctive spiralling signature, "L. C. Charlesworth, General Manager, Eastern Irrigation District." Graciously, Charlesworth thanks Robertson for his letter of the previous day, and, as he has no desire to add further to "the existing serious friction," he agrees to vacate his desk for the present. However, Charlesworth makes it quite clear that he does not consider the trustees' dismissal to be valid, and that he will be available to return to his desk and position on 24 hours' notice from them. Within a half-hour of Robertson's call to Mullen, Charlesworth left town.

Perhaps the difficult burden of that day's events was lessened somewhat by a later call to Robertson from Henry Dahl, one of the trustees. He agreed that Robertson had had no choice but to carry out Mullen's instructions, and reassuringly stated that the former board members, Mr. Charlesworth, and 90% of the local settlers were "behind him" in his difficult role as official trustee. "No matter what took place," Dahl said, Robertson's position with the District would be safe.

OTHER CONCERNS

There was to be one more day of intrigue before Robertson was allowed to turn his attentions to the work-a-day business of the District. On April 21, Mullen again telephoned, this time requesting information on the District's policies with regard to the Rolling Hills Project, the joint PFRA-EID settlement undertaking. From the types of questions asked it seems that Mullen may have been looking for "irregularities" in the board's handling of this situation. As well, it is apparent that Mullen was not yet well-informed as to his duties and responsibilities as a member of the Irrigation Council. He seems to have believed it necessary for the Council to approve all applications to lease lands in the project before settlement could begin. Robertson corrected him on this point. Such approval was needed only for purchase contracts — not for leases.

That same day, April 21, W. E. Cain, MLA for Bow Valley and a Brooks clothier, stopped Robertson on the street to inquire as to the whereabouts of Mr. Charlesworth. He took this opportunity to apprise Robertson of the part he, Cain, had played in the whole matter. Without explaining why he would be sent a copy of Plunkett's interim audit, Cain informed Robertson that, immediately upon its receipt, he had advised the board to conduct their own inquiry into the alleged "irregularities." When they took no such action, Cain felt it "his duty to bring the matter to a head by having the government investigate."

Gov't Has No Desire
To Take Over E.I.D.
Says Low At Brooks

Probe at Brooks
May Open May 22

(By Our Own Correspondent)
Edmonton, May 8

Tentative date for opening of sittings of the royal commission, composed of Judge J. A. Jackson, of Lethbridge, to investigate "alleged irregularities" in operations of the Eastern Irrigation District, is Monday, May 22, George B. Henwood, K.C., deputy attorney-general, stated today.

The sittings are to commence at Brooks, and are expected to be concluded there. G. M. Blackstock, K.C., of Medicine Hat, is counsel for the commission.

THE INQUIRY GETS UNDERWAY

Within the next few days, a corps of lawyers descended upon the EID headquarters. Preliminary to the actual hearings, they began the process of collecting information for the inquiry by examining records and querying staff members.

G. M. Blackstock was to act as counsel for Judge Jackson, the Commissioner. W. H. McLaws and Samuel Short appeared for E. L. Gray and the board of trustees. Mr. Huckvale and Mr. Plunkett, the provincial auditor and his assistant, were also on hand.

Those must have been very hectic and emotionally exhausting days for Robertson and the rest of the District staff, as they scurried about, fetching accounts, letters and other documents for the lawyers and auditors. And how could they possibly make room for all those extra bodies?

Finally, on May 8, a Royal Commission was issued to Judge John A. Jackson, and the actual sittings of the investigation commenced in Brooks on May

Movie theatre doubled for many years as an assembly hall. Setting for 1939 inquiry into "serious irregularities."

29. Held under the jurisdiction of the Public Inquiries Act, the hearings involved the calling and recalling of a great many witnesses. District employees were constantly on call to bring out documentary evidence. Finally, after accumulating 1,710 pages of testimony and 304 exhibits, and at a cost to the taxpayer of over $10,000, the inquiry concluded on July 11. Later that month, His Honor, Judge Jackson's summary report was prepared and submitted to the Lieutenant-Governor of Alberta-in-Council.

RESULTS AND RECOMMENDATIONS

The inquiry established the existence of irregularities in some of the EID's policies and practices. Commissioner Jackson stipulated, however, that he used the word "irregularity" in its broadest sense, referring to practices which affected the District and the general public in a potentially harmful way. A number of the acts of the board and manager were found to be outside their statutory powers, a situation which might have had very serious consequences had it been allowed to continue. Jackson recommended that the District should concern itself exclusively with operating the irrigation system and promoting colonization. He cautioned that it should not lend money or otherwise offer financial assistance to industries "not directly connected with irrigation . . . except as specially authorized by law and then only under proper safeguards."

On the other hand, Jackson was fully cognizant that

. . . the Board and the Manager, Mr. Gray, saw the necessity for retrenchment in every line, otherwise the district would run behind, as did the CPR before it. They were not so much concerned with the means as to the ends to be gained. They evidently thought that 'many a pickle makes a mickle'. As Mr. Anderson said, they were not afraid to cut corners where necessity arose. The final results would appear to justify the means, but nevertheless the Board and Mr. Gray did not fully realize that their powers were not inherent but were limited entirely by legislative enactment. They should have approached the government for assistance. There was nothing particularly to be proud of in the actions of the board in this regard. I do not think they fully realized, in their innate honesty, that if the principle of doing what they thought best without regard to proper authority were adhered to, the results might eventually be disastrous to all concerned, especially if followed by others not so honest.

After four years of "co-operative management," Jackson described the District as being "in splendid shape."

As part of the inquiry, the commissioner made himself available to receive opinions from local residents. Some complained about the management of the system but most expressed high praise for the trustees and manager. One formal resolution was presented, probably by representatives of the Rainier UFA Local. In part, it stated that government "investigation or interference" in the District's affairs should only be undertaken if approved by a majority vote of water users. As Jackson pointed out, this ignored the wider importance — to the entire province — of irrigation projects. He defined the EID as "not merely a private enterprise." Rather it is more appropriately viewed as a "perpetual trust," vested by the Crown in successive boards of trustees but, in the final analysis, accountable to the taxpayers of the province.

Jackson Reports On E.I.D. Probe

ONLY HONEST IRREGULARITIES

FOUND IN E. I. D.

Board and Manager Cleared of All Possible Suspicion of Theft, Graft Or Personal Dishonesty, Says Jackson

'On the Whole, District Has Been Managed Remarkably Well.'

POLITICAL INFLUENCE

Another resolution put forward by the UFA local stated:

The Irrigation Council should be composed of technical advisors and should not be a political body and no contract holder of any Irrigation District should be a member of the Council.

The target of the above statement was undoubtedly Solon E. Low, who would have been judged unqualified on three counts had the standard suggested by the farmers prevailed. First, he was a Social Credit cabinet minister and, therefore, subject to political motivation; second, he was a former teacher, and unlikely to qualify as a technical advisor in irrigation matters; and third, he had recently purchased a large farm just northwest of Duchess, making him a contract holder in the District. His fellow councillor, D. B. Mullen, was also a cabinet minister. Both were suddenly appointed to the Irrigation Council just after the EID contracted with Charlesworth to assume the job of general manager. The contrast between the qualifications of these two men and those of L. C. Charlesworth is striking.

Trained as a civil engineer at the University of Toronto, Charlesworth later did extensive work as a surveyor. Since 1915, he had held various provincial civil service positions at the level of deputy minister. His direct involvement with irrigation dated from 1921 and included drafting amendments to the Irrigation Districts Act, and the positions of Chairman of the Irrigation Council, Official Trustee of the Lethbridge Northern Irrigation District, and Director of Water Resources.

THE CALGARY HERALD, WEDNESDAY, MARCH 29, 1939

Can William Tell?

When they first heard of the government's actions, many local residents were enraged by what they saw as manipulation of their District's affairs to serve political ends. Subsequent events did nothing to change the original perception that political conniving was afoot. Although it was adamantly denied by all members of the Socred caucus, from Premier Aberhart on down, there were many, even beyond the borders of the EID, who shared the local farmers' suspicions. Charges were levelled by some that the government's actions were motivated by a desire to discredit E. L. Gray and, through him, the Liberal party.

Others felt that the trustees' refusal to hire a man of the government's choosing as general manager was the spark that set off the string of allegations against them. The attempt, on the part of the government, to influence the board's choice of a general manager was viewed by some as a move towards annexation of the District. It was suspected that, with their own man in the top administrative position, the government hoped to dominate decision-making at the EID.

Thwarted in this plan by the board's determination to stick with Charlesworth as manager, the government then, according to popular belief, appointed an official trustee. This was seen as the first step in a take-over bid.

The government already had control of several smaller, less financially-sound irrigation districts. Had their allegations against the board and manager been proved, it would have given them the perfect excuse to assume control of the solvent EID. Thus ran the common suspicion.

The Legislative Assembly served as an arena for accusations from both sides of the house. The daily newspapers relished every charge and countercharge. But it was in the staid atmosphere of Judge Jackson's hall of inquiry that the case was, at last, impartially heard. His findings categorically cleared the board of trustees and E. L. Gray of "all possible suspicion of theft, graft or personal dishonesty . . . The evidence disclosed nothing dishonourable."

BACK ON AN EVEN KEEL

L. C. CHARLESWORTH

Eventually, the District regained its autonomous status. As returning officer, George Robertson supervised the election of a new five-member board of trustees on November 17, 1939. Voter turnout was high, and all three of the previously-ousted trustees were returned to office. They were joined by two long-time District farmers, Jens Block of Millicent and Ralph Burrows of Countess.

L. C. Charlesworth, who had doubtless been quietly biding his time until he considered it advisable to return to his desk at the EID headquarters, actively assumed the general managership on December 6, 1939. George Robertson's long stint as official trustee was finally over. Ironically, the Irrigation Council in the person of Mullen, suggested it would be "fitting" for the EID to pay Robertson an additional $100.00 per month to compensate him for his extra responsibilities as "Official Trustee and General Manager."

E. L. Gray's parting advice to the District farmers was to view the discord, in which they had all been swept along, as a mere passing event in the life of a great project. As Charlesworth took up the reins, the period of tribulation drew to a close and the EID entered a period of relative stability.

The steady, predictable growth that characterized the EID's operations in the first half of the 1940's was due, in no small measure, to the influence of its general manager. Aged sixty-six when he took on the job, Charlesworth, with the respect and co-operation of the board, instituted programs and policies of great benefit to all areas of the District. To this end, contact men were appointed to represent the particular views of each locale.

Under proper authorization of the Irrigation Council, advances were made to several agricultural marketing concerns. Rosemary Co-operative Dairies, for instance, obtained some District funding to set up a cheese factory in 1940. By the time of the co-operative's fourth annual meeting, the producers had repaid their debt and were financially independent.

Although the war-time economy caused prices for agricultural commodities to sky-rocket up from their Depression depths, maintenance of production levels was hampered by a severe labour shortage. Many farmers were in military service. Charlesworth was instrumental in arranging for prisoners-of-war, most of them members of the German Merchant Marine, to make up the labour shortfall. This program was first instituted in the fall of 1943 and was still in operation in 1946, some time after hostilities had ceased.

After the completion of five-and-a-half years' service, Charlesworth left the EID's employ in the spring of 1945. Awarded an Honorary Doctor of Laws from the University of Alberta in 1950, Dr. Lionel Clare Charlesworth died in September of 1956, at the age of eighty-three.

ROLLING HILLS PROJECT

Of the many programs which bear the stamp of Charlesworth's clear thinking, there is one which provides an especially good example of the positive results attributable, at least in part, to his long-term planning ability. The Rolling Hills Project was a joint undertaking of the Eastern Irrigation District and the Prairie Farm Rehabilitation Administration of the federal Department of Agriculture. Although Charlesworth was not directly connected with the EID in 1937, the year

Early Rolling Hills settlers from Saskatchewan drylands.

in which the preliminary agreement was signed, he was an influential member of the planning committee that mapped out the various phases of the program's implementation. As chairman of Alberta's Irrigation Council, Charlesworth's approval was necessary before the EID could embark upon such a venture, and, after he became general manager of the District, he had first-hand knowledge of the project, which was an almost-instantaneous success.

Credit for the initiation of the Rolling Hills Project belongs, however, to E. Leslie Gray, Charlesworth's predecessor as manager. Although Gray's status as leader of the Alberta Liberal Party may have been a factor in the trials and tribulations experienced by the District in 1939, it had at least one positive effect. Gray was on a tour with Hon. J. G. "Jimmy" Gardner, federal (Liberal) Minister of Agriculture in the early summer of 1937. In his capacity as head of the PFRA, Gardner was visiting some of the more sparsely-settled areas of the province, with a view to relocating several hundred farmers from unsuitable lands in Saskatchewan and Alberta. After they had visited northwestern Alberta, Gray was able to convince Gardner to come further south. So impressed was Gardner by what he saw of irrigation's benefits in the EID, that he readily agreed to PFRA's collaboration in colonizing the hitherto-undeveloped Rolling Hills area of the irrigation system.

Comprising about two townships in the extreme southwest corner of the EID, the area is well-suited to irrigation. The soil is a fertile sandy loam, and the topography level. The CPR's preliminary surveys of the system revealed its irrigation potential; and during the period of major construction just prior to World War I, they constructed the necessary major structures to deliver water to the area. But the expected tidal waves of settlers never materialized; and because of its rather remote location, the Rolling Hills division was never colonized.

Never, that is, until the necessary settlers, were assisted by the PFRA to make the move from dryland to irrigation farming. A small group arrived each year, from 1939 until 1945. In that period, a total of 152 new settlers had taken up quarter-section parcels. Of this number, only 16 subsequently signed quit claims and left. Those who stayed experienced a fair degree of success, even in their first one or two years.

In 1949, after the Rolling Hills colonization project had been underway for a scant ten years, it was described by Charles S. Burchill, the noted University of Alberta economist, as "solidly established and prosperous." In his historical survey of irrigation development, Burchill attributes the project's remarkable success to "three factors of policy" and "one fortuitous factor."

> In the first place, the very low price charged for irrigated land was probably the most important single factor in ensuring the success of the project. From the first, there was every prospect that the farmer could become the owner of the land and of all improvements which he placed upon it. The incentive to improvement was strong and the rapid increase in the productivity of the district reflects the power of this incentive.

If, at the expiry of the two-year lease, the settler wished to remain at "The Hills," he took out a land contract similar to those signed by other District residents. The regular $10-per-acre price of irrigation land was reduced to $8 by direct application of the PFRA grant to land prices.

> In the second place, the high proportion of experienced irrigators on the project ensured to every inexperienced man a neighbor on the adjoining farm who could supply advice and assistance.

Realizing that successful irrigation farming requires instruction and practice in certain skills not at all necessary in dryland farming, the EID stipulated that the northwest quarter of each section be reserved for settlement only by experienced irrigators. Many of those who took up these lands were the up-and-coming sons of older EID residents, but some came in from other irrigation districts.

> In the third place, the very careful selection of settlers, and the preparatory work done in breaking and levelling land, both reduced the hardships of pioneering, and ensured that the pioneers who had to submit to these hardships would be of a type not easily discouraged.

Applications to settle at Rolling Hills were handled by a three-man committee of experienced EID employees. After meeting stringent economic and experience requirements, applicants were granted a two-year lease. Although the value of all initial land development was added to the price of their land, the fact that over half of each quarter-section was ready-broken allowed first-year settlers to get right to the business of planting their crops. If the crops failed, it would not be because of late planting. The availability of irrigation water ensured adequate moisture. At least two of the many variables of good agricultural production were working in the settlers' favour.

> The fortuitous factor was the accident which established the settlement at a time when the prices for agricultural products were rising more rapidly than farming costs. No better time could have been chosen to initiate such a project than 1938-40.

OTHER SETTLEMENT

People of many nationalities have contributed to the growing population of the District in its 50-year history. Most numerous among these are the Japanese-Canadians. During World War II, these people were subjected to what, in hindsight, seems extraordinarily harsh treatment at the hands of the Canadian government. Because of their racial origins, irrespective of their declared allegiance to Canada, many had their West Coast properties confiscated, and suffered internment and arbitrary relocation to the interior of the country.

The sugar beet fields of southern Alberta offered a livelihood to many of the displaced. In 1942 and 1943, others came to the EID to find employment as farm labourers.

The end of the war brought a close to a shameful period in our country's history, but it was several more years before the ban denying land ownership to the

Japanese-Canadians was relaxed. By this time, those who had worked on the irrigated land of the EID were aware of its potential. It was reasonably priced, so many families purchased farms, mainly in the Rosemary and Rainier areas, and settled here.

Some of these, who were experienced market gardeners, began to specialize in the growing of potatoes and were instrumental in introducing this crop to the District.

Local potato grower wins awards at Royal Winter Fair, Toronto, 1967.

Family of Dutch descent operates this modern, self-contained dairy.

Holland was the homeland of a second group which filtered into the EID in the post-war years. Like the Japanese-Canadians, the Netherlanders arrived by way of the farm labour network. In a few years, many of this group were able to purchase land of their own. By the early 1950's, available land parcels were scattered throughout the District and, as a result, the famed industry of the Dutch farmers is noticeable in many areas of the EID.

The reader will recall that, when settlement of the CPR's irrigation block was first attempted, the aim was to establish colonies of people of like religious and ethnic origins. Over the years, these early settlements were much diluted by the infusion of a mixture of people from diverse backgrounds. In the mid-1950's, however, this colony system was reintroduced to the area by the Hutterian Brethren, or Hutterites.

Young Hutterite women donate refreshments at Brooks blood donor clinic.

Springside Colony, located northeast of Duchess, was, in 1954, the first Hutterite colony to be established in the EID. Soon afterwards, the Newell and Bow City settlements were founded. Since then, three more colonies (two of which are extensions of the initial ones) have been set up in various parts of the District.

The Hutterian Brethren were part of the Anabaptist movement which arose in Europe in the late 16th century. Named for their leader, Jacob Hutter, they adopted a communal way of life, based firmly upon religious doctrines. To escape persecution, they came to North America about the turn of the 20th century, locating colonies in Montana, Saskatchewan and Alberta.

Originally attracted to the EID by available land and the higher productivity possible through irrigation, the Hutterian colonies now own almost 70,000 acres (28,000 ha), of which 2,888 acres (1,169 ha) are irrigated.

Recognizable by the sombre tones of their simple, old-fashioned dress, the Hutterites are noted for their efficient large-scale farming operations. In addition to raising extensive field crops, the colonies, which strive for self-sufficiency, devote substantial acreages to market gardens and carry on diversified livestock production.

DEVELOPMENT AND EXPANSION

The buoyant war-time and post-war Canadian economy was responsible for a period of great expansion in the EID's operations. Over 150,000 acres (60,700 ha) were on the water rolls, and the percentage of water rates in arrears was steadily decreasing. Although there were a few minor problems, the general mood in the District was one of heightened optimism for the future. In this vein, the board of trustees put forward a proposal, which was enthusiastically endorsed by the water users at the ninth annual meeting in the spring of 1944, to earmark an expenditure of up to $5,000 yearly to attract ". . . suitable industries . . . to provide markets for the class of products which . . . must be produced on irrigated lands to ensure success."

To implement this new policy, the board hired a man whose sole responsibility was to promote the EID as an ideal site for agricultural processing industries. E. W. (Ted) Brunsden was a University of Alberta graduate in agriculture. Although he was a city boy from Ontario, he had some experience with a grain marketing organization and had worked as a district agriculturalist for several years. After arriving in Brooks, he immediately began to develop useful personal contacts and prepare promotional literature.

No one was more enthusiastic about this "new phase of development" than L. C. Charlesworth. As he retired from the general managership in the spring of 1945, he made glowing predictions of things to come:

> I believe that the soundness of this project has now been established beyond question and that the District is about to enter upon a new phase of development and expansion the limits of which are impossible at present to foresee but which I am sure will be very wide.

E. W. BRUNSDEN

Obviously Brunsden made a very good impression in his first few months with the District. After Charlesworth had given the board notification of his impending retirement, the general managership was offered to Brunsden. During his two-year period at the helm of the District, he enjoyed some measure of success — both in attracting agricultural processors to the EID, and in encouraging the greater crop diversification necessary to provide the industries with raw material.

A vegetable cannery was established at Brooks in 1946. For just over ten years, it processed locally-grown table peas and corn. Then, a fire forced its closure. At Bassano, also in 1946, the Southern Alberta Dairy Pool began operating both a creamery and honey processing plant. A second facility run by this same firm made locally pasteurized milk available in Brooks for the first time.

And the elusive beet sugar factory was again pursued. EID officials and other local interest groups mounted a fund-raising effort in early 1946. In a short space of time, almost half a million dollars had been raised for development of a sugar beet co-operative. One year later, a tentative deal between producers and manufacturers fell through and all funds were returned to the subscribers. This marked the final chapter in the great EID sugar factory romance.

After leaving the EID, Ted Brunsden, like E. L. Gray before him, entered the political arena. While Gray had represented the Liberals in the Legislative Assembly of Alberta, Brunsden became the Conservative member of the Parliament of Canada for the Medicine Hat riding.

CARL J. ANDERSON

Brooks Studio.

Because of his early and long-time involvement with the EID board, and his experience as a farmer and rancher in the area, the board chose Carl Anderson as its fourth general manager. He, too, was involved in promoting agricultural diversification in the District but, whereas Brunsden had concentrated his efforts on growing specialty crops, Anderson focused on livestock-related aspects.

Soon after he began farming in the Scandia area, Anderson became convinced of the advantages of including livestock as an integral part of farm diversification. He was one of the founding members of a co-operative shipping association on the Bow Slope in 1929, and was later an impassioned promoter of feeding co-ops and community pastures.

During his tenure as manager, which extended until 1964, the District took a very active part in encouraging area farmers to expand and improve their beef cattle and sheep herds. To this end, it participated directly in feeding associations and constructed and operated livestock sale yards at Bassano and Brooks. Anderson never lost sight of the fact that the EID was operated by the farmers for their collective benefit and he saw livestock programs as the primary means of improving local prospects.

As was mentioned above, the EID became directly involved with livestock early in its existence. At that time, the District's primary purpose was to provide a mechanism for acquiring land payments and water rates from its cash-poor settlers. This soon proved impractical — partially because it failed to take cognizance of several of the factors necessary for a viable livestock-based economy.

In the late 1940's, when the District again involved itself in livestock dealings, it undertook a comprehensive program of livestock development in all areas of the region. This program was in effect throughout the Fifties and well into the Sixties, providing the foundation for the EID's current livestock economy.

The success of our livestock industry rests on four factors:

1) availability of adequate financing, whether to purchase animals for fattening only, or to establish or enhance herds;
2) the existence of surplus or otherwise-unsaleable crops to serve as winter
   feed;
3) the availability of low-cost grazing land which can provide summer
   pasture for herds; and
4) a local marketing facility which is located close to producers and which
   sells a quantity of animals sufficiently large to attract the volume of
   buyers necessary to establish and maintain prices.

All four of these aspects were included in District policy — and that policy
was acted upon to encourage a growing number of EID farmers to become
livestock producers.

Although the 1940's were more prosperous than the 1930's, farmers were
still, by-and-large, a cash-poor bunch. Banks, at least those located in the EID,
considered them to be extremely poor credit risks. Few individual farmers obtained farm operating loans of any size from the usual lending institutions;
therefore, the District encouraged the development of feeder associations. These
co-operative groups provided small producers with the opportunity to pool their
resources and, backed by partial government guarantees, obtain a line of credit.
The directors of each association, in turn, made "loans" to their members. During
the thirty-five years that feeder associations functioned as "the farmers' bankers,"
many producers were given the opportunity to establish flocks of sheep or herds of
cows. Others used association funds to improve their herds or increase their
numbers.

The first feeder association in the EID was the Bow Valley group, who
formed in 1938. South Slope, Tilley-Rolling Hills, East Bow Valley and, finally,
the non-government-backed Brooks Central group all were active at various times.
Among them, they accounted for millions of dollars of livestock business that
would not otherwise have been done. In more recent times, the association's
function of loaning money has been taken over almost completely by commercial
lending institutions. In the less prosperous post-war agricultural economy,
however, the feeder associations played a major role in establishing livestock
production as a profitable and integral part of farming in the EID.

Once the farmer had obtained his livestock, he then needed sufficient feed to
fatten them for market. This was seldom a problem in the EID because, under
irrigation, the District as a whole usually produced a surplus of most commodities. Even in years when crops were weather-damaged and therefore, unsaleable, they could be used for livestock feed and, in this way, provide a measure
of financial return.

Another form of feed, readily available in the EID, is grass. With the
establishment of community grazing associations in the late 1940's and early
1950's, use of District-owned grasslands became available to all qualified water
users. This development served to enhance the area's livestock-producing capacity even further, and provided the means for more farmers to keep larger herds. As
one Brooks businessman put it, "Because of the grazing associations and EID

grasslands, buying a farm in the EID is like having a small ranch included in the price!"

Producing feed grains and forage crops, and having the wherewithal to purchase livestock to consume these nutriments can only be successful if producers have an efficient channel for marketing. Prior to the EID's establishment of livestock auctions in Brooks and Bassano, a local livestock operator could sell in one of two ways, neither of which could be counted upon to bring a consistently fair price for his stock. If he sold to an itinerant buyer who came to the farm gate, he would save the costs of transporting his animals to market, but there was no competition for his product in this method. It was, therefore, extremely difficult to persuade the buyer to up his offer by more than a small fraction. It was a "take it or leave it" proposition.

By shipping to a larger centre, the farmer could probably get a better price; but shipping costs, especially for the small producer, had a way of eating up the profits. Banding together with his neighbours in a co-operative shipping association was one way to reduce transportation costs and get a fair return. Shipping associations were organized in the District in the late 1920's and operated effectively for many years.

Carl Anderson's extensive involvement with livestock shipping and feeding associations made him very aware of the marketing problem faced by producers. It was one of his primary concerns as general manager and led to the establishment of two EID-owned and locally-run auction yards.

These facilities brightened the marketing picture. In addition to resident livestock farmers and local feeder associations, they attracted big buyers from larger centres. With this outside presence, competition increased and so did prices. The margin of profit was further widened by the fact of lower transportation costs. Whether he hauled his own animals or paid a local trucker to do the job, the farmer's transportation costs were substantially reduced.

Another benefit of local sale yards was the employment opportunities they afforded. Some of these were directly involved with the running of the auction marts. Additional economic effects were felt in all sectors of the business community. Producers began to come from further afield to sell their livestock in the EID; and soon, they were doing a good part of their business here. Local merchandising and service establishments expanded to meet the demand.

Although the health of the EID's livestock base is subject to the cyclical

Some of CPR's horses, near Brooks, 1923.   Poultry yard, Cassils, 1930.

Crowd at 1957 bull sale, Brooks.

At the Brooks stockyards, 1963.

EID encouraged winter fattening of livestock in 1940's and 50's.

swings that characterize livestock economies everywhere, its current vitality is due, in large measure, to the far-sighted District policies first instituted almost forty years ago.

During the post-war era, there were new developments in many other threads of the EID's fabric of life. Because all areas of endeavour are interdependent, expansion in the agricultural sector brought about a general expansion in the community. The historical development of two particular sectors, schools and municipal government, are outlined below.

SCHOOLS

Very few schools existed here until after World War I. As colonization of the CPR's Eastern Section gathered momentum, however, school districts were formed. The chart provides information on the 23 districts which had been organized by 1924. They are listed under the irrigation system's six operating divisions.

Three of these were consolidated districts, which meant that all children in the area attended one central school. Because many lived at some distance from the school, they were brought to and from classes in a horse-drawn, canvas-covered school van. These vehicles were often crowded, and cold in winter — except for the lucky ones who got on first and took the choice places next to the small stove — but they were a boon to many a cash-poor parent. By taking turns at driving the school van, local residents could work off their school taxes, and perhaps earn some extra cash to pay other bills or purchase what would otherwise be unattainable luxuries.

These small rural school districts continued to collect their own taxes and operate their own local schools until 1938. In that year, all the schools within the recently formed irrigation district (with the exception of Brooks) were encompassed by one large jurisdiction. The EID School Division, No. 44, first established its headquarters at Bassano, and at a later date, relocated to Brooks. Until it was amalgamated with the County of Newell in 1953, the EID School Division retained responsiblity for all schools except those in the Town of Brooks. Gradually, country schools closed down and pupils were transported via motorized school buses to larger centres. In the 1940's, dormitories were operated in a few EID communities, to house students from outlying areas while they attended high school. Today, the County of Newell's school system has an enrollment of almost 1,500 students. There are schools in eight hamlets and villages, plus five one-room schools located on Hutterite colonies.

Brooks School Division No. 2092 was established in 1911. At that time, the borders of the school jurisdiction encompassed the small settlement along the railway track, as well as much of the surrounding prairie, on which a few farmsteads were beginning to appear. Today, these boundaries remain virtually intact, but the size of the population living within them has skyrocketed — both in the town and rural areas. The six schools of the system are all located right in Brooks and 2,400 students are enrolled.

There are also a number of private religious schools in the area.

SCHOOL DISTRICTS IN EASTERN SECTION
SEASON OF 1924

BASSANO DIVISION

BASSANO	SCHOOL DISTRICT		TOWN OF BASSANO
LATHOM	do	do	do do LATHOM
BURN BRAE	do	do	NE¼ 18-21-17-4
CLEMENCEAU	CONS'L'D. SCHOOL DISTRICT		SE¼ 17-21-16-4
ROSEMARY	do	do do	TOWN OF ROSEMARY
GEM	do	do do	NE¼ 36-22-17-4

DUCHESS DIVISION

ALLAN CAMERON	SCHOOL DISTRICT		SW¼ 26-21-15-4
WEST DUCHESS	do	do	NE¼ 36-20-15-4
DUCHESS	do	do	TOWN OF DUCHESS
WELLMAN	do	do	NE¼ 16-21-14-4
CLANCY	do	do	NW¼ 4-20-14-4

BANTRY DIVISION

PRINCESS	SCHOOL DISTRICT		NE¼ 17-20-12-4
HADDINGTON	do	do	TOWN OF PATRICIA
MILLICENT	do	do	do do MILLICENT
SUTHERLAND	do	do	NE¼ 2-19-14-4

BROOKS DIVISION

BROOKS	SCHOOL DISTRICT		TOWN OF BROOKS
CASSILS	CONS'L'D. SCHOOL DISTRICT		NW¼ 5-19-15-4

TILLEY DIVISION

TILLEY	SCHOOL DISTRICT		SW¼ 24-17-13-4
RENFREW	do	do	NE¼ 35-16-13-4

BOW SLOPE DIVISION

JENNY LIND	CONS'L'D. SCHOOL DISTRICT		NW¼ 8-15-15-4
BOW SLOPE	SCHOOL DISTRICT		SW¼ 27-16-16-4
ALCOMA	do	do	SE¼ 24-16-16-4
KITSIM	do	do	SE¼ 16-17-16-4

A GRIFFIN
Supt. Operation & Maintenance

MUNICIPAL GOVERNMENT

Because large-scale settlement of the shortgrass prairie region was delayed until after 1910, the area of what is now the EID lacked sufficient population to organize rural self-government. By the late Teens, seven improvement districts (No's. 124, 154, 155, 184, 185, 186 and 216), each comprising an area of about nine townships, were in existence. Under the authority of the provincial Department of Municipal Affairs, of which Lionel C. Charlesworth was then Deputy Minister, these organizations were authorized to assess taxes. Their responsibilities included road construction and maintenance, as well as provision of health care.

In 1918, it was made compulsory for all local improvement districts to reorganize and incorporate themselves as rural municipalities. There was great resistance to this change in many areas of the province, as it was widely assumed that the tax burden would increase significantly under the new system. Nevertheless, some regions were interested in developing this type of organization. In May 1919, the minutes of the UFA Local in Brooks record that the Secretary was instructed to obtain information on forming a municipality. The following month, a decision was taken to work toward that end.

Perhaps, like so many decisions, this one was not acted upon. Or perhaps, a rural municipality actually was formed, but, as was common throughout the province, it was still referred to as an improvement district. In any case, whatever their official designation, the early 1920's found all municipal authorities busily engaged in collecting taxes so they could improve local conditions. The establishment of the Alberta Department of Public Health in 1919 had provided for the inauguration of hospital districts, so health matters were no longer of direct concern to the improvement districts. Instead, they concentrated their efforts on building more and better roads and agitating for the completion of promised railway spur lines and the extension of the telephone system to rural areas.

Local settlers who wished to save their meagre cash for other purposes could do roadwork to pay their taxes. Their assessment would be credited at the rate of 25¢ per hour for a man, and 50¢ per hour for a man and his team. Horse-drawn slips and fresnoes were used to construct and maintain the few miles of proper dirt roads that connected the major local settlements. Individual farms were serviced (and the term is used loosely) by bone-jarring trails that followed the fence lines, or meandered out across the wide prairie spaces between pockets of agricultural settlement.

When the Dirty Thirties rolled around and Hard Times were everywhere, most improvement districts had all they could do to keep their financial heads above water. Those in irrigated areas fared better than ones in dryland regions. In the latter, the improvement districts were drained by providing relief; however, destitute families were less numerous in the irrigated areas of the province. A 1934 listing of the financial resources of all the local municipalities located in the CPR's Eastern Section shows that even the least prosperous, I.D. 185, had $907.00 on hand. I.D. 124 was pretty flush with $16,964 in the treasury.

The year 1935 saw the amalgamation of all the local I.D.'s into one large organization, Improvement District No. 123. A few years later, when the government renumbered all the I.D.'s in the province, it became I.D. No. 28.

Ten years later, improved economic times in the area led to the formation of a more autonomous form of self-government. The municipal district of Newell, No. 28 held its first elections for municipal councillors in 1948. Its offices were established in an addition to the EID headquarters building.

The County Act of 1952 provided the opportunity for rural municipalities in Alberta to undertake a new form of organization. The M.D. of Newell commenced negotiations with the EID School Division and the local Agricultural Service Board, with the objective of amalgamating their jurisdictions into one consolidated municipal government. On January 1, 1953, the County of Newell became fourth in the province to adopt the county system.

At this time, municipal services were expanded to include more than the traditional road building and maintenance. Today, weed inspection, roadside grass cutting and general farm information are the major responsibilities of the county's Agricultural Service Board. Road building, maintenance and drainage are the concerns of the nine-member council, who represent the residents of all hamlets and rural areas within the county's borders. The councillors also constitute the school board in the County of Newell, and have responsibility in the environmental health area (landfill sites, sewer facilities). Through joint inter-municipal agreements with other local authorities, the county is involved in recreation, library, and fire protection services.

Separate municipal governments exist in the incorporated villages (Duchess, Rosemary and Tilley) and towns (Bassano and Brooks). These are located within the county's geographical boundaries which correspond almost exactly to those of the EID.

Until September of 1966, when the County of Newell building was officially opened, all municipal government offices were housed in the EID headquarters building.

County of Newell building.

FARM INCOME SQUEEZE

With the arrival at the half-century mark, the Eastern Irrigation District entered difficult economic times. A number of factors interacted to produce an agricultural recession, the equal of which had not been felt since Depression days.

Perhaps the most significant of these was that wily old gambler, the weather. Farmers everywhere are prey to its vicissitudes. Irrigation guarantees sufficient moisture to grow good crops but water is only one component of climate. For much of the decade of the Fifties, other elemental forces vented their collective wrath on western Canada.

The danger of hail is always of concern to farmers, which is why a hail insurance scheme was established early in the District's history. In the 1950's, the threat became a wide-spread reality. Crops suffered extensive damage as hailstorms cut wide and savage swaths across the EID. Before long, the hail insurance fund was decimated, leaving farmers with no hope of compensation.

Killing frosts also wreaked havoc with agricultural production. In normal times, the EID is blessed with a long growing season but, especially throughout the first half of the decade, frost often shortened it at both ends. This resulted in further heavy crop losses. Specialty crops, such as vegetables, were severely attacked. Even hardy strains of alfalfa, which had been grown successfully for over thirty years, were no match for the succession of long cold spells. In 1959, most of the District's alfalfa winterkilled forcing closure of the area's first alfalfa dehydrating plant. This left little forage for farmers to feed their own livestock, let alone sell to their usual markets outside the District.

It was a time of wicked blizzards. In 1951, a prolonged spring storm, accompanied by heavy snowfalls, killed off large numbers of livestock. Because it was well into May before the runoff had subsided, planting was extremely late. Other years, fall blizzards arrived to interrupt harvest. In 1954, Christmas was near when the last of the crops was taken in.

Wes Crook, District Engineer, using survey rod to measure 1939 snowdrift. Winter blizzards in 1950's were equally severe, especially in 1951.

Grain and forage crops damaged by bad weather are almost impossible to market, so many local farmers used their unsaleable crops for livestock feed. They reasoned that, when the fattened animals were sold, some income, at least, would be realized to meet water rates and other commitments. But troubles rarely come singly and the beef cattle industry was entering on hard times, too.

By the early Fifties, the EID's agricultural economy had become firmly based upon the livestock industry, with cow-calf operations being the most popular endeavour. Because the bottom had fallen out of the wool market and cheaper frozen lamb was being imported from New Zealand, sheep production was declining. However, there were still many thousands raised in the District each year.

The table below provides the EID's livestock census data for selected years from 1941 to 1955. Over that fifteen-year period, the numbers of beef cattle had increased by over 200%, while there was an overall decline of 44% for sheep. Dairy cattle remained unchanged.

EID LIVESTOCK CENSUS
SELECTED YEARS, 1941-1955

	Beef	**Sheep**	**Dairy**
1941	21,000	55,000	3,500
1948	30,000	42,000	3,500
1953	42,000	21,000	3,500
1955	49,000	31,000	3,500

Source: *Eastern Irrigation District Twenty-First Annual Report*, 1955, p. 2.

The growth in the beef industry had signalled a healthy trend toward diversification of the farmers' income sources but, in 1952, progress in the livestock economy hit a very solid roadblock. An outbreak of the dreaded foot and mouth disease spread like grass fire throughout western Canada. Embargoes were imposed on the shipping of beef. Many farmers had to slaughter their entire herds. Right about that time, diversification into beef cattle must have seemed a *very* bad idea, indeed.

Shrinkage of farm income was simultaneous with an increase in input costs. Post-war technological innovations presented the farmer with a number of ways to enhance production. These included agricultural chemicals, mechanized land levelling and a range of new, high-powered farm implements. Inevitably, taking advantage of these improved services and commodities entailed heavy expenditures. Such investment was not always prudent, as it did not necessarily result in increased production adequate to cover the additional input costs.

Rural electrification, accompanied by many plug-in household and workshop appliances, tempted the consumer to "live better electrically." At a price. Consumerism threatened to run rampant and the stigma against living beyond one's means faded.

The dictum that the whole is greater than the sum of its parts is aptly applied to the situation which prevailed in the EID at this time. Just as a rise in expenditures was accompanied by a decline in income at the individual farm level, the same cost-price squeeze was adversely affecting the affairs of the District as a whole.

Further complicating the situation was a growing conviction among some water users that failure to pay water rates was an insignificant matter. Some, perhaps, felt helpless to deal with the multitude of factors eroding their once-healthy income. Others may have become complacent. The EID had been providing them with a great many services for a long time; many, unthinkingly, may have expected that this state could continue indefinitely, even if few farmers were able, or willing, to pay their water levy in full each year.

The EID of the 1950's, unlike that of the 1980's, was almost totally dependent upon water rates to finance its operations. Government grants were very infrequent and small-scale. Compensation payments from oil and gas companies were negligible. Investment income was channelled into a reserve fund for the replacement of large irrigation structures.

As more and more water users defaulted on their water rates, the District found itself in a stranglehold. In 1950, for the first time in its fifteen-year history, the EID dipped into the interest from the reserve fund to give farmers a break on their water rates. This measure had little overall effect. Past-due water rates mounted up. For most of the 1950's, the amount outstanding hovered around the half-million dollar mark. In 1956, an unprecedented total of 22 farms were repossessed by the District and sold under the rate enforcement provisions of the Irrigation Districts Act.

Better weather conditions in 1958 and 1959 resulted in a slight improvement in collections but, on the occasion of its silver anniversary, the District's financial position was still quite precarious. The annual report for 1959 contains a chart graphically depicting the seemingly impossible situation in which the District was attempting to operate.

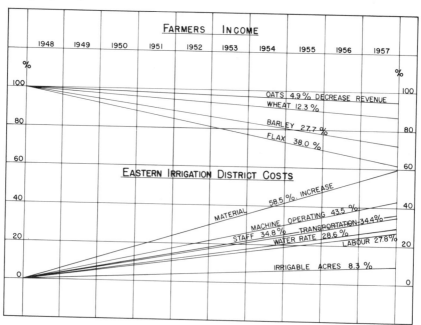

Between 1948 and 1957, farmers experienced an average revenue decrease of more than 20 per cent for the four crops shown. Over the same period, their water levy had *increased* by almost 30 per cent. Although other components of total input costs are not graphed, it is certain they increased proportionately.

Five major segments of the District's input costs for the period are displayed; not surprisingly, all show a steep rise. The average increase in operating costs is almost 40 per cent. It was obviously impossible for a 28.6 per cent increase in water rates, even taking into account the augmenting of the water rolls by 8.3 per cent, to make a dent in the burgeoning costs. Even had all water users been able to pay their water rates in full every year, the District would still have been forced to operate at a deficit.

The EID viewed this situation as difficult, but not desperate. An improvement in the agricultural economy was probable and would bring with it a return to equilibrium in the District's day-to-day operations.

However, another development, the creeping debilitation of the irrigation system's aging structures, was reaching crisis proportions. If the major structures were not overhauled very soon, the system threatened to crumble to a gradual halt. Massive injections of funds were needed to prevent its decay.

The EID could not possibly raise the necessary money independently. It would have to come from a larger constituency. At this point in the history of the District, the phase of government investment was introduced.

EID sprayers were used to treat cattle against warble flies, later for weed control.

Courtesy, Ira Lapp.

EID D-6 cat plowing snow, 1945. Non-irrigation-related services contributed to costs of operation.

GOVERNMENTS INVESTIGATE IRRIGATION

In 1935, after 20 years of operation, the water delivery system of the Eastern Irrigation District was still considered to be state-of-the-art. However, by the 1950's, although the system still functioned with relative efficiency, the larger structures were showing signs of severe stress. Repairs to the Brooks Aqueduct were an on-going necessity and incurred substantial expenses yearly. The footings were in poor condition and EID engineers feared for the general safety of the structure. Portions of Bassano Dam were in a similarly weakened state. The need for extensive rehabilitation work became increasingly urgent, if the system were not to deteriorate gradually into obsolesence.

Water shortage problems, experienced throughout the system in dry years, consistently plagued some parts of the District. To rectify this situation satisfactorily, it would be necessary to improve the storage and delivery networks, which would entail the construction of large and expensive reservoirs and considerable rehabilitation of the main canals.

By careful management, the EID had built up a reserve fund of $1 million for the replacement of capital assets. This was but a drop in the proverbial bucket insofar as the costs of major reconstruction were concerned. There was no way that the water users could raise the large amounts of money needed, so they turned to the government for assistance.

To this time, although both senior levels of government were involved in irrigation in Alberta, no comprehensive policy for the development and perpetuation of the several water systems had been put in place. In the early stages of irrigation in the West, the federal government encouraged private investment in large projects. Direct assistance came through the offices of the Department of the Interior, in the form of topographical surveys and land classification programs. When it transferred control over all natural resources to the Government of Alberta in 1930, the federal government withdrew its influence entirely for a time. The Water Resources Act passed by the Alberta Legislature in 1931 superceded the Northwest Irrigation Act. With the enactment of this provincial law, control and regulation of its water resources became Alberta's responsibility. Since rivers have no respect for the imaginary lines man draws to describe his territory, the Prairie Provinces Water Board was established in 1948 to ensure that Alberta, Saskatchewan and Manitoba each receives an equitable portion of the river flows that originate in the Rocky Mountains.

The Prairie Farm Rehabilitation Administration appeared on the scene in 1935. It was formed by the federal government to attempt to deal with the desperate problems experienced by western farmers in the Depression years. The enlightened programs of the PFRA are credited with reclaiming millions of acres of debilitated prairie lands and putting them back to productive agricultural use. It follows quite naturally that an agency charged to rejuvenate poorly-used lands would be supportive of the development of irrigation to render arable the land in arid regions. Through the PFRA, small grants had been given to the EID for assistance with reservoir building — Cowoki, One Tree, Rock Lake — and towards the construction of the Antelope Creek Fill. The settling of Rolling Hills area was a joint accomplishment of the District and the PFRA. Other irrigation districts were aided to a similar extent by the federal agency.

The role of the Alberta government had been, by and large, of an advisory and regulatory description, although financial assistance had been given to some of the irrigation districts. Not all of these were so fortunate as the EID in inheriting a ready-made water delivery system. The province backed bond issues for the construction of several community-instigated irrigation projects. When their water users found themselves in financial difficulties, unable to repay the bonds, the government was foced to abandon its arm's-length policy and settle the debts. In these cases, an official trustee was appointed to oversee the affairs of the indebted district.

In the years following World War II, government participation in irrigation grew. The Bow River Development, now the Bow River Irrigation District, began operation in 1920 as the British-financed Canada Land & Irrigation Company. It limped along for 30 years until it was taken over by the Canadian government in the 1950's. The purchase price was minimal, approximately $2.5 million, but over $50 million were expended, through the agency of the PFRA, to update and expand the system. As a part of the total effort, the province developed what was known as the West Block of the project.

The St. Mary and Milk Rivers Development was another joint project of the two governments. It involved extensive enlargement of the old Alberta Railway and Irrigation Company water system which had originally been built by Galt Enterprises in the late 1890's and taken over by the CPR in 1912. The system was transferred to the Alberta government in 1946. The PFRA began construction of the St. Mary Dam in 1948.

Although water delivery from this system was inconsistent because of a lack of water storage facilities, it was not the desire to improve its efficiency, per sé, that brought the Canadian government into the act. Rather, it was the pressing need to capture Canada's share of the international waters before they flowed on through into the United States. As with the Bow River Development, large expenditures of federal and provincial moneys were made on this project.

The investment in these two new schemes was lavish in the extreme, especially when compared with the limited funds available to the longer-established irrigation projects. The older irrigation districts began to question government policy. To them, it seemed unreasonable to extend irrigation to additional lands, some of which required extensive preparation in order to make the best use of irrigation, while allowing to decay those systems that had proved to be of substantial benefit.

In 1946, the Alberta Irrigation Projects Association was formed to "represent the views and discuss problems peculiar to irrigation districts in Alberta." The efforts of this group, supported by petitions from the individual districts, prompted the Alberta Minister of Agriculture, Leonard C. Halmrast, to appoint an Irrigation Study Committee. Albert T. Johnson, who had been on the EID Board from 1941 to 1954, was one of its three members. The Committee filed its report in September of 1958. The following was one of many recommendations made: "[that] Uniformity be established in the form of organization and in policy of government assistance." The report foresaw that "a logical pattern for irrigation development and administration is emerging."

Harry E. Strom became Minister of Agriculture in 1962. Those in the EID who worked with Strom praise him for his acute understanding of the problems facing the province's irrigation districts and for the dominant role he played in effecting the measures needed to arrive at a co-ordinated and comprehensive policy in the field of irrigation. Under the Agricultural Rehabilitation and Development Act, various agencies took part in a series of studies designed to relate the costs of irrigation to the benefits derived from it and, thereby, provide the groundwork for decision-making by both federal and provincial authorities.

The several phases of the investigation were compiled as "Alberta Irrigation Studies." The Eastern Irrigation District was selected to serve as the case model. With 30 per cent of the total irrigated lands in the province, it was the largest of the irrigation districts and had been financially solvent for almost 30 years.

Initially, three main objectives were outlined. The first was to assess how much it would cost to rehabilitate the system. This phase was conducted by the Engineering Branch of the PFRA. The Economics Branch of the federal Department of Agriculture undertook the second phase of the study, to determine the extent of the additional income derived from irrigation in relation to the heavy costs it incurs. The final line of enquiry dealt with the distribution of benefits from irrigation: to the farmers it serves, the surrounding locality, the province and the nation. This was done by the Department of Agricultural Economics, University of Alberta.

Field work of the PFRA engineers led to the conclusion that, to assure delivery of adequate water to all users, a program to replace or rehabilitate most of the major structures of the EID should be implemented without delay. Thirty-five major structures, in addition to the Bassano Dam and the Brooks Aqueduct, were identified. Early replacement of the Brooks Aqueduct was advised and repairs vital to the extension of the life of the Bassano Dam were outlined. Of the remaining larger structures, they judged some to be temporarily adequate; others — the Lathom Flume, the Crawling Valley Flume, two outlet structures on Lake Newell and the headgates on the North and East Branch Canals — required prompt rebuilding.

An appendix to the PFRA report suggested a five-year reconstruction program, giving priority to the most acute problem areas.

The maintenance program that had been carried out by the EID on the secondary distribution structures — over 6,000 checks, drops, chutes, culverts, small turnouts, etc. — was judged by the PFRA to be of a high standard. These structures were gradually being replaced, often with the aid of Winter Works Program funds, with the more durable materials of metal and concrete being substituted for much of the original timber. The District was optimistic that, although the laterals were in need of attention, satisfactory care could be given to them in future.

The EID was fortunate in that, unlike some of the other irrigation districts, its drainage network, constructed by the CPR, was relatively efficient. Since 1935, the operating and maintenance staffs had built additional spills and greatly improved the drainage at the farm level.

Generally, it can be expected that interest groups in the resource sector will vie for government assistance in the furtherance of their development. There are a number of possible ways in which the contents of the public purse can be allotted; and, therefore, it is, or certainly should be, imperative that the choices made by government embody the greatest good for the largest number of its citizens. For this reason, before deciding to substantially increase their investment in irrigation, both the federal and provincial governments had to be satisfied that its financial benefits would be distributed far beyond the borders of the irrigation districts. If large investments in an irrigation system would benefit only the farmers whose lands were watered, it would be obviously unjust to ask other taxpayers to contribute.

To arrive at a direct cost-benefit ratio, the Economics Branch of the Department of Agriculture weighed the value of production output against the input costs necessary to attain it. This comparison was made for two separate situations: under irrigation in the EID and under simulated dryland conditions. The study concluded that the costs incurred for irrigation projects are compensated for, three times over, by the direct benefits to be derived from them. On that basis alone, additional government investment in the system was justifiable.

The University of Alberta's contribution to the study showed that, if the EID continued to cover its own operating costs, the distribution of net benefits would be as follows: the irrigation farmers — 11%; the local area — 22%; the province — 32%; and the nation — 35%. It is clear from this breakdown that the labours of an EID farm family have economic impacts far afield.

Data obtained from the study of the EID were then applied to the other irrigation projects in the province. Reports of the "Alberta Irrigation Studies" ran to seven volumes. They were proof positive that irrigation was a sound investment. Although the wheels of government often turn slowly, it was a foregone conclusion that eventually new policies would produce the necessary funds to give irrigation a new lease on life.

The Alberta Irrigation Projects Association provided a meeting ground and fostered a strong sense of co-operation among the disparate districts. Working together, they were able to identify common concerns and present a consensus in negotiations with governments. The EID Board of Directors and their general manager, R. T. White, were closely involved in all dealings with government. White assumed the position of Chairman of the AIPA in 1965.

The "Alberta Irrigation Studies" culminated in 1967 with policy recommendations drawn up by the Alberta Department of Agriculture. Many of these were implemented in the Irrigation Act of 1968 which incorporated and repealed all earlier Acts governing irrigation in Alberta. The new legislation standardized the administrative and operational procedures of all 13 irrigation districts. Because of these changes, the governing body of each district was now referred to as a board of directors, rather than trustees.

GOVERNMENT INVESTMENT IN IRRIGATION

It was 1969 before the event, toward which all irrigationists had been working for so long, actually occurred. It was in that year that provincial government funding for the rehabilitation of irrigation structures was initiated. The moneys were provided on a cost-sharing schedule by which the province paid 86 per cent of costs and the irrigation district, 14 per cent — whence comes the familiar "86-14 Formula." Equitable distribution of the funds among the districts was pro-rated upon irrigable acreage and water rates in each. From 1969 to 1975, the government contributed $10,549,260 to the rehabilitation program. Of this amount, the EID received $2,611,983.15, while paying $425,386.44 as its share.

Since 1975, cost-sharing has continued on the same percentage basis, but under the title of Irrigation Rehabilitation and Expansion Program. With the aim of the program widened to include the building of structures (principally reservoirs) to expand existing systems, more money was allocated. Funding now comes from the Alberta Heritage Savings Trust Fund in two separate streams. Each branch is administered by a separate government department. Rehabilitation work continues under the Irrigation Capital Works (ICW) Program, for which the Irrigation Council, Department of Agriculture is responsible. Alberta Environment administers the Irrigation Headworks Program, designed to replace or reconstruct principal intake structures.

Works that fall under the mantle of the ICW Program include seepage control, canal and lateral relocation, canal rehabilitation, pipeline installation, and reservoir construction. Government cost-sharing has permitted the establishment of an orderly schedule to update the system. The total amount expended, in the EID on this program, since its inception in 1975, is $35,439,133.30 from the Government of Alberta and $5,769,161.37 from the EID. Coupled with the amount expended in the years between 1969 and 1975, in all $44,245,664.26 has been spent to modernize the irrigation system. The benefits are reflected in the increased efficiency with which water is conveyed to the farms of the District.

Concurrent with the on-going provincial funding programs, large capital construction projects have been undertaken by the federal government. Following the PFRA's examination of the structures of the EID system in 1963, the engineers found that replacement of the Brooks Aqueduct was critical to the effective operation of the system. More than a decade elapsed before an agreement was made between the Canadian and Alberta governments to deal with the federal government's role in the unfolding irrigation story. It was not until 1979 that water was diverted into the newly-constructed earth-fill canal which took the place of the obsolescent aqueduct. Bassano Dam is, at present, undergoing complete rehabilitation. The total design and construction costs of these large projects has been assumed by the PFRA and amount to some $22,000,000.00.

Such generous infusions of government money into irrigation improvements has emphasized the importance of liaison between the districts and officials of the various funding agencies. The Alberta Irrigation Projects Association has elevated communication with government representatives to the highest level of importance among its activities. Regular meetings among the district members, and with civil servants and elected government people, encourage an exchange of information on matters of mutual interest and concern.

In 1983, as almost 20 years had passed since the time of the "Alberta Irrigation Studies," the AIPA commissioned research into irrigation's current impact on society. The study indicated that irrigation activities account, directly and indirectly, for the employment of 35,000 Albertans, and contribute about $940 million to the province's annual gross domestic product. These data were influential in persuading LeRoy Fjordbotten, the Minister of Agriculture, to concentrate his efforts on securing the continuation of the Rehabilitation and Expansion Program after its 1985 expiry date. Happy reverberations resounded throughout southern Alberta when his announcement on the subject was delivered. He confirmed the extension of the program for a further five-year period; $30 million will be made available annually to continue the rehabilitation and expansion programs.

R. T. WHITE

Through most of the period of significant government assistance to irrigation districts, Robert T. White was at the helm of the EID. He is the nephew of W. Tait White, who was a member of the Small Committee at the time of the formation of the farmers' organization. White, the uncle, lived with the family of White, the boy. The latter may be said to have cut his teeth on the bones of contention between the farmers and the CPR.

White was the first native son ever to be employed in the position of general manager and chief engineer. His father was an irrigation farmer and White was raised in the District. Following active service in World War II, he began his career with the EID, as a summer student from the University of Alberta where he was studying civil engineering. He returned to Brooks when he graduated to work as an engineer for the District until 1963, at which time he was promoted to assistant general manager and chief engineer. White had the distinction of being the first employee to work his way up through the ranks to the top job in the organization.

He is described, by those who know him, as an innately political animal. This quality served him well in his several years as a negotiator on behalf of the EID and the Alberta Irrigation Projects Association. Often, the successful outcome of discussions with government officials depended upon a firm consensus among representatives of the 13 diverse irrigation districts. White's skill and influence as a mediator contributed to the maintenance of good relations among group members and constructive progress in dealings with funding agencies.

H. A. CAMPBELL

General Manager consults with Manager of Administration, left, and District Engineer, right.
Photographer: K. Kimura.

When White took early retirement in 1983, he was succeeded by Harvey A. Campbell, the current general manager. Born in a Saskatchewan farming community, Campbell has had wide experience in the construction industry. After several years of operating his own company in the interior of British Columbia, he came to Calgary to accept the position of construction manager for the building of the Deerfoot Trail road-complex. In securing the services of Campbell, the EID Board of Directors considered his knowledge of the construction sub-trades to be most helpful in these days of expansion and rehabilitation of the irrigation works.

RECENT REHABILITATION AND CONSTRUCTION

Bridge from CPR days re-used on Bow Slope Canal rehabilitation.

East Branch Canal check structure exposed for rehabilitation.

Fabriform chute in the Imperial Colony.

Underwood McLellan Ltd.

Buried canal liner for seepage control.

Typical pre-cast concrete check drop being back-filled.

Inlet structure to Crawling Valley Reservoir.

Modern compaction equipment being used on Brooks Aqueduct fill.

Constructing earth coffer dam at Bassano Dam to allow rehabilitation of gates.

THE FUTURE

Unfortunately, even blessed with ready money, expansion of irrigation in the EID is limited, at present. Suitable sites for internal storage have been quite thoroughly exploited. Although the Cowoki-Tilley, Kitsim and Crawling Valley reservoirs have assured delivery to parts of the District where, previously, shortages were a problem, their construction has resulted in the addition of only a limited number of new acres to the water rolls.

At the time of the Bow River Development in the early 1950's, the EID became concerned that, with a growing demand for water from irrigation projects and power-producing facilties, the District would experience water shortages and be unable to assure delivery to the farmers. It was then that the board and manager first began to press the government to consider the construction of on-river storage dams. Since that time, several studies have been done to locate possible sites.

Questions arise about the environmental impact of such developments. Many authorities agree that they would have few, if any, harmful effects. In fact, they would conserve water — a resource that we are gradually realizing is in finite supply. On-river storage facilities can be made deeper than reservoirs on land; therefore, water stored on the river has much less surface area from which evaporation takes place than the same amount of water stored in a shallower land reservoir.

What on-river storage reservoirs would mean for irrigation in the EID is entirely positive. The Bow River's water supply comes from melting snows and heavy rains that fall in the front ranges of the Rocky Mountains. This means that the river flow is seasonally inconstant and, oftentimes in a dry year, not entirely reliable.

Upstream of the EID inlet are a number of other major users: two other irrigation districts, the City of Calgary and TransAlta Utilities. Water available to the EID is contingent upon the demands of these consumers, as well as upon climatic variations. Several times in the past, the District has suffered deficits during peak irrigating times. On-river storage structures would make it possible to collect water at times of high flow, and store it for use in those times when the stream is sluggish. This would stabilize the supply of water to the EID system and allow for the inclusion of significant additional acreage under irrigation.

From 1974 until very recently, largely because of inadequate water supply but also to halt land speculation during the days of the oil boom, there has been a moratorium on irrigation development in the EID. Water users were permitted to extend irrigation only on quarter-sections that were already under the ditch. No other parcels could be entered on the water rolls.

A commissioned report, *"The Eastern Irrigation District Study,"* which recommends methods for more efficient use of water available to the EID, coupled with the assurance of a constant supply of water from the new Crawling Valley Reservoir, moved the Board to accept applications for new irrigation development. Unfortunately, it will not be possible to assent to all the requests that were received.

The Alberta Department of Agriculture has set the ultimate expansion of irrigation in the District at 550,000 acres (222,750 ha). At present, 245,000 acres (99,225 ha) are irrigated and the District is optimistic that, with careful conservation measures, an additional 65,000 acres (26,325 ha) may be adequately served. To reach the ultimate goal suggested by the Department of Agriculture figures, we must come full circle in this discussion — to on-river storage, augmented by enlargement of the overall capacity of the internal reservoir complex.

In the meantime, and in the absence of the ideal situation, the EID continues to work toward improvements of the existing system with the resources at hand.

The acute pangs suffered by the system when it thirsts for water drive home the importance of doing our utmost to conserve what water we have at our command. This dictum applies to the management and staff of the EID and, also, to the District's farmers.

With an open channel system such as the EID's, much of the water allotted for irrigation is, in fact, lost before it can be applied to crops. Measurements of water use show that only 57 per cent of the nearly 600,000 acre-feet diverted annually from the Bow River at Bassano are of direct agricultural benefit. Industry, municipalities, Ducks Unlimited Projects and stock watering-holes use another 6 per cent of the flow. The remaining 37 per cent is lost to the system through evaporation, seepage and spill. This last statistic is not quite so negative as it looks; two-thirds of this water is later returned to the Red Deer and Bow Rivers, thereby rejoining the South Saskatchewan River System.

It is some consolation to know that this portion of the EID's water allotment is not irretrievably lost to the common resource stock. However, it is only sound economic practice to adapt as high a proportion of our water as possible to our own benefit.

Evaporation draws considerable moisture from the water, on its long run from the inlet to each and every field. Pipelining of the larger channels is not practical, but much water loss through evaporation could be counteracted through the pipelining of the smaller channels of the system. At that level, the cost would not be prohibitive.

A certain amount of spillwater is unavoidable. This is why drainage is as vital as water delivery to a smooth-functioning system. Carelessness may cause excessive amounts of water to simply move through the system, their only contribution being a negative one of wear and tear on the channels that convey them. The reclamation of spill water is now being effected at several points throughout the District. Pumping is employed to recycle, back into irrigation, water that otherwise would be lost.

Seepage, which has been an inseparable companion of irrigation since its beginnings, may be combatted with canal linings. Concrete tile liners were used in the District while the CPR was still operating the system. This is an expensive material which precludes its wide-spread use. Liners made of other materials — fiberglass, asphalt and sulphur — are being tested by provincial agricultural researchers. To date, in the EID, the most economical and satisfactory canal lining material used is a water-impervious clay. At sites where this clay is unavailable, plastic lining buried beneath the canal bed has been found to be an effective method for controlling seepage.

Although seepage is often a farmer's headache, there are instances when it has healthy side-effects. On pasture, it may stimulate the growth of native and tame grasses. The Kitsim Project is an experiment by Ducks Unlimited Canada to measure the effects of water storage basins on grazing lands.

The proliferation of well-designed sprinkler systems has brought about a basic change in irrigation farming. Lands which once would have benefitted only marginally from gravity irrigation are now yielding bountiful crops under a sprinkler. The even application of water in controlled amounts alleviates many problems of inadequate drainage and salinity. At the same time, it conserves water.

The extensive rehabilitation programs carried out by the EID in the past two decades have reduced water wastage. So too, has the control of weeds in the ditches, although some controversy has arisen over the Districts use of herbicides. Reclamation of farm lands has resulted from the rehabilitation programs. Canal realignment has been made possible through the modernization of machinery and construction techniques. No longer does the contour of the land completely dictate canal placement. As far as is practical, when a canal is reconstructed, it is aligned on the boundary of a quarter-section parcel of land, leaving the main part of the field free of obstruction.

As more is learned of the optimum relationships of water, soil, and climate to the plant-life they nourish, the future will doubtless see changes in the cropping practices in the EID. Agriculture in Alberta is a complex mosaic of inter-dependent segments, and co-operative efforts are required to derive the maximum benefits from each of them. The costs attendant upon irrigation farming reduce the profit margin on crops that could be grown equally well on dryland. With the advantages of adaptability that result from irrigation, to say nothing of the wider range of crops it will support, it is reasonable to expect that the irrigation sector of the agricultural industry will alter its production to complement, yet contrast with, those of dryland farms.

Co-operation is imperative, too, in arriving at policy decisions with regard to our water, a commodity more precious than gold. Every effort should be made to prevent our struggles over its disposition from deteriorating into an unthinking rush to gain control.

Water is a resource we hold in common and, whatever our special interests, we all stand to lose unless we can come together and work out a long-range blueprint for its equitable distribution and conservation.

EPILOGUE

Bolstered by the farsighted policies of governments, the District has every reason to approach the coming years with confidence. Thanks to the skill of the CPR engineers, we have been blessed with a well-designed irrigation system. In the past two decades, with generous monetary and technical assistance from the people of Alberta and the rest of Canada, through the agencies of the federal and provincial governments, we have succeeded in refining the efficiency of the system to a high degree. The importance of irrigation to the agricultural wealth of our nation is now undisputed. By a five-year extension of its participation in rehabilitation programs, the province has re-endorsed its commitment to bring Alberta's water-delivery systems to an advanced technological state, unsurpassed anywhere in the world.

It is important never to lose sight of the fact that we, in the District, are the producers of the basic commodity of life — food. We play a leading role on the world stage. We are indeed fortunate in the knowledge that, if we adopt sensible management and conservation practices for our resources, our future prosperity will be guaranteed.

With good fortune comes responsibility — to husband well the gift of good land and to make the very best possible use of the nurturing waters of our irrigation system. If we succeed in this aim, when the centennial of the EID rolls around, our children and grandchildren will look back with the same degree of pride and gratitude that we, on this our 50th Anniversary, accord those who preceded us.

MEMBERS OF THE BOARD, EASTERN IRRIGATION DISTRICT 1935-1985

Alberts, Don (Millicent)
Director: 1979 and 1980
Chairman: 1981 to 1985
Anderson, Carl J. (Scandia)
Chairman: 1935 to 1940
Barg, F. (Duchess)
Director: 1974 to 1979
Barnes, Gordon (Millicent)
Director: 1963 to 1965
Berg, Rand (Millicent)
Director: 1973 to 1978
Block, V. Jens (Millicent)
Director: 1939 to 1945, 1950 and 1951
Burrows, Ralph M., Sr. (Countess)
Director: 1939 to 1953
Chomistek, Joe (Scandia)
Director: 1981 to 1985
Colbens, Colben O. (Tilley)
Director: 1946 to 1950, 1952 and 1953
Dahl, Henry (Duchess)
Director: 1935 to 1940, 1947 and 1948
Chairman: 1941 to 1943
Daniels, Robert C. (Rolling Hills)
Director: 1955 to 1962, 1973 to 1977
Chairman: 1963 to 1972, 1978 and
1979
Fuller, H. (Countess)
Director: 1975 to 1980
Garrow, Alexander (Brooks)
Director: 1941 to 1942
Giles, D. (Cassils)
Director: 1980 to 1985
Graham, James H. (Rainier)
Director: 1962 to 1964
Henrickson, Harvey (Patricia)
Director: 1951 and 1952, 1954 to 1961
Chairman: 1962
Hofmann, Earl (Scandia)
Director: 1965 to 1972, 1976 to 1980
Chairman: 1973 to 1975
Hollinda, John (Tilley)
Director: 1973 to 1979, 1981
Chairman: 1980
Huber, Reuben (Rosemary)
Director: 1962

Johnson, Albert T. (Brooks)
Director: 1941 to 1943, 1954
Chairman: 1944 to 1953
Jorgensen, Ove H. (Gem)
Director: 1972 to 1974
Larson, Arthur (Rainier)
Director: 1953 and 1954
Mortensen, William (Tilley)
Director: 1982 to 1985
Owens, George (Rainier)
Director: 1944 to 1947
Peltzer, Rudy F. (Rosemary-Duchess)
Director: 1974 and 1975, 1978 to 1985
Chairman: 1976 and 1977
Penner, George I. (Rosemary)
Director: 1954 to 1961
Petersen, Soren C. (Tilley)
Director: 1955 to 1969
Plumer, Ben E. (Duchess)
Director: 1969 to 1971
Rust, Norman J. (Millicent)
Director: 1948 and 1949
Ryan, Milton J. (Gem)
Director: 1963 to 1968
Scott, Robert (Tilley)
Director: 1935 to 1940
Sherman, Elwood P. (Duchess)
Director: 1966 to 1972
Stringam, Bryce C. (Rosemary)
Director: 1950 to 1953
Chairman: 1954 to 1961
Stringam, G. Owen (Rosemary)
Director: 1949
Thomsen, D. W. (Rolling Hills)
Director: 1980 and 1981
Veenstra, Jake (Rolling Hills)
Director: 1982 to 1985
Wagstaff, Fred (Rolling Hills)
Director: 1945 and 1946
Walde, John (Gem)
Director: 1981 to 1985
Wester, Odd Ralph (Tilley)
Director: 1970 to 1972
Woodward, George W. (Brooks)
Director: 1943 and 1944

GLOSSARY OF SELECTED TERMS

Aqueduct — A large-capacity flume. See Flume.

Arable — Land classified as suitable for growing cultivated crops.

Assessment Roll or Water Roll — A record of each parcel of land within an irrigation district, which contains acreage classification (i.e. "to be irrigated" or "other"), pertinent water agreements and annual per-acre irrigation rates.

Automatic Control — Adjustment of a water control mechanism, accomplished without manual on-site operation.

Balancing Pond — A water management reservoir designed to conserve temporary excess flow from canals, for later release.

Canal — An open channel built to convey water. These are designated, in order of decreasing capacity, as: Main (Primary or Supply); Secondary; Distributary; Lateral; and ditch.

Carrying Capacity — Maximum number of animal units that a specific land area can support. One mature cow, with or without an unweaned calf, is equal to 1.00 animal unit.

Deep Tillage — The practice of tilling cropland, using a cultivator or disc, to a depth of 4-6 in. (10-15 cm). This method is more common in irrigation farming than in dryland farming, where shallower tillage and rod-weeding are more often used.

Distribution System — See Irrigation System.

Diversion — (1) The process of taking water from a stream or other body of water; or (2) The structure which is used for this purpose.

Drainage — The return of excess water (either from natural run-off or irrigation spill) by means of a system of man-made channels and natural drains.

Evapotranspiration — The transfer of water from the earth's surface into the atmosphere, by the dual processes of evaporation from the air and transpiration from plants.

Fill — A man-made earthen embankment built up to carry an irrigation canal across a valley or depression of land.

Flume — A structure built to convey water across a valley or along a hillside.

Gate — A structure used to regulate irrigation flow in response to seasonal demand. Examples: headworks, headgates, sluice gates, turnout.

Glacial Till — A mixture of geological materials, ranging in size from boulders to clay particles, which was eroded and transported by glaciers. (Strahler, 1975).

Headworks, or Headwork — Headworks has recently been defined by the Provincial Government as the entire main canal system from the water source or diversion right up into a major internal storage reservoir. Also, see Gate.

Irrigable — A classification of agricultural land to which it is physically possible to convey and apply irrigation water, and which offers a reasonable return on irrigation development.

Intake — A structure which allows irrigation water to flow from a canal or reservoir into a pipeline or pumping unit.

Inverted Siphon — An airtight pipe used to convey water by gravity across a valley or depression of land, or under a railroad or highway.

Irrigation District — A not-for-profit body created and governed under the Irrigation Act, Chapter I-11, Revised Statutes of Alberta, 1980. Its major purpose is to convey water for irrigation and it has the power to levy charges on its water users. It also operates and maintains the water delivery system, and undertakes the attendant administrative functions.

Irrigation Rates, or Water Rates — An annual charge set by the Board of Directors of an irrigation district and levied upon each acre of land within the district which is classified as "to be irrigated".

Irrigation System — A network of channels and ditches built by an irrigation district or company to convey water from a source (usually a diversion on a river) to locations where it can be used for irrigation farming.

Moisture Deficit — The difference between the annual amount of precipitation that is needed for satisfactory crop growth and the amount of rainfall actually available to plants. The amount of precipitation that falls is reduced through evaporation by wind and sun and by percolation through the soil, so not all of it reaches the growing plants. The annual moisture deficit in the EID is 8 in. (200 mm). Irrigation is used to offset this deficiency.

Off-Stream Storage — Water stored in a place other than the valley of a naturally-occurring flowing stream.

On-Stream Storage — Water stored in a location confined to the valley of a flowing stream.

Percolation — The loss of precipitation and applied irrigation water by downward movement through the soil to the water table.

Pipeline — A long, enclosed irrigation canal situated below ground level.

Rehabilitation — The process of restoring the components of an irrigation system, by completely rebuilding the original irrigation works. This process may be carried out on headworks, structures and/or canals and ditches. Such reconstruction can be utilized either to restore the works to their original form or capacities, or to modify their location, flow capacity or other features.

Reservoir — An artificial lake constructed to store irrigation water. Usually a reservoir is sited in a naturally-occurring depression of land. To ensure that the water remains confined to the reservoir site, dams or embankments are then constructed across all low points.

Riparian — On, or pertaining to, the banks of a watercourse or lake.

Ripping — The practice of passing a series of cultivator shanks (spaced 18″-24″ [46-60 cm] apart) through the soil at a depth of 14″-24″ (36-60 cm). The purpose is to improve water penetration and soil structure by shattering hard soil layers.

Riprap — Broken stones or rocks, placed on the upstream slopes of an embankment for protection against the action of water particularly against the effects of wave wash.

Seepage — The gradual movement of water away from an irrigation structure or body of water.

Siphon — An airtight pipe which makes use of natural air pressure and gravity to convey water over a hill, a ridge of land, or a man-made structure. (Archaic spelling — syphon).

Solonetzic — A type of soil occurring mainly under grass or grass/forest cover in semi-arid or subhumid climates and characterized by abnormal concentrations of sodium.

Specialty Crop — An agricultural commodity possessing all of the following characteristics: (1) sold into a limited market; (2) production requires specialized management; (3) relatively new and grown on a limited acreage within a given locale; and (4) has several alternate markets, of which the Canadian Wheat Board is *not* one.

Spill, or Spillwater — Water in excess of that required by the canal system, or by irrigation of crops. Spillwater is returned eventually to the river via the drainage system.

Spillway — (1) A natural or man-made channel used to remove spillwater; or, (2) a feature constructed to convey excess water over a dam.

Storage Capacity — The volume of water which may be impounded or enclosed by a reservoir, or behind a dam or embankment. When storage capacities for reservoirs in the EID are quoted, the figure refers to the volume of water usable for irrigation purposes (live storage). Dead storage is non-usable water.

Structure — A concrete, metal or wooden component of an irrigation system built to control water levels. Examples: checks, check drops, chutes, controls and drops.

Turnout — A structure within a canal through which a diversion of water is made, usually into a canal of lesser capacity.

Water Delivery System — See Irrigation System.

Water Rates — See Irrigation Rates.

Water Roll — See Assessment Roll.

Water User — The owner or purchaser of a parcel of land which is recorded on the assessment roll of an irrigation district as containing one or more acres classified as "to be irrigated".

REFERENCES

Publications and Communications of: Agriculture Canada; Prairie Farm Rehabilitation Administration; Environment Council of Alberta; Government of Alberta; Eastern Irrigation District.

BIBLIOGRAPHICAL NOTE

In doing the research for this book, the authors consulted a wide variety of sources. Among the published materials we found useful were local community history books. Many standard reference works on the development of the Canadian West were also consulted.

CPR, EID and government documents were of much help in outlining the development of our area — from turn-of-the-century topographical surveys and reports, up to the most recent economic studies and irrigation policy statements.

Much of our information was found in periodicals: *The Brooks Banner, The Bassano News, The Brooks Bulletin, The Calgary Herald;* technical journals; and magazines.

Aspects of EID development have been studied by several researchers at universities and other cultural institutions. Of these studies, we found E. Alyn Mitchner's manuscript, "Western Waters", particularly helpful. Taped oral histories were also used in piecing together details of our earlier history.

For those interested in doing further research on the Eastern Irrigation District, the complete bibliographical index compiled by the authors is available in the EID Archives and Library in Brooks. The EID collection also includes copies of many of the reports, files and other papers which were germane to the completion of this book.